HowExpert Guide to Show Pigs

101+ Tips to Learn How to Breed, Raise, and Prepare Show Hogs for Pig Shows

HowExpert with Keiren Cook

Copyright HowExpert™
www.HowExpert.com

For more tips related to this topic, visit
HowExpert.com/showpigs

Recommended Resources

- HowExpert.com – Quick 'How To' Guides on All Topics from A to Z by Everyday Experts.
- HowExpert.com/free – Free HowExpert Email Newsletter.
- HowExpert.com/books – HowExpert Books
- HowExpert.com/courses – HowExpert Courses
- HowExpert.com/clothing – HowExpert Clothing
- HowExpert.com/membership – HowExpert Membership Site
- HowExpert.com/affiliates – HowExpert Affiliate Program
- HowExpert.com/jobs – HowExpert Jobs
- HowExpert.com/writers – Write About Your #1 Passion/Knowledge/Expertise & Become a HowExpert Author.
- HowExpert.com/resources – Additional HowExpert Recommended Resources
- YouTube.com/HowExpert – Subscribe to HowExpert YouTube.
- Instagram.com/HowExpert – Follow HowExpert on Instagram.
- Facebook.com/HowExpert – Follow HowExpert on Facebook.
- TikTok.com/@HowExpert – Follow HowExpert on TikTok.

Publisher's Foreword

Dear HowExpert Reader,

HowExpert publishes quick 'how to' guides on all topics from A to Z by everyday experts.

At HowExpert, our mission is to discover, empower, and maximize everyday people's talents to ultimately make a positive impact in the world for all topics from A to Z...one everyday expert at a time!

All of our HowExpert guides are written by everyday people just like you and me, who have a passion, knowledge, and expertise for a specific topic.

We take great pride in selecting everyday experts who have a passion, real-life experience in a topic, and excellent writing skills to teach you about the topic you are also passionate about and eager to learn.

We hope you get a lot of value from our HowExpert guides, and it can make a positive impact on your life in some way. All of our readers, including you, help us continue living our mission of positively impacting the world for all spheres of influences from A to Z.

If you enjoyed one of our HowExpert guides, then please take a moment to send us your feedback from wherever you got this book.

Thank you, and we wish you all the best in all aspects of life.

Sincerely,

BJ Min
Founder & Publisher of HowExpert
HowExpert.com

PS...If you are also interested in becoming a HowExpert author, then please visit our website at HowExpert.com/writers. Thank you & again, all the best!

Table of Contents

Chapter 1: The Art of Breeding Show Pigs

This chapter will focus on the breeding aspect of pig production. This is where you will learn about different types of pigs, what sow to choose, how to make sure your sow is in heat, pick a boar, breed your sow, house them, etc. This is a dense chapter with a lot of knowledge, but all of it is necessary for an individual interested in breeding their own stock.

The Different Breeds

Tip 1: Know the breeds of pigs

There are many different breeds of pigs out there, across the country, and in other parts of the world. The four main breeds that have shown to be the most successful in shows and meat production are Berkshire, Hampshire, Yorkshire, and Durocs. These are the most popular breeds seen at shows across the country, with Hampshire and Yorkshire taking the lead at most popular purebred hogs. Each of these breeds has its own physical and behavioral qualities that make them unique and useful in different ways. When it comes down to it, the Yorkshire is the longer breed with a leaner stature that is beneficial for creating a hog that will produce a larger pig in terms of length. Yet, due to their longer build, they have a bigger area to create muscle mass, leading to less defined muscle compared to other breeds. The Hampshire is the heavyweight champion of the pig world. They are shorter in length but wider in build with broad shoulders, deep rib spread, and a more defined rump for ham size. Yet these hogs are shorter, so ultimately there is less bacon and loin with the shorter underline and topline. The Durocs are wide all the way through their build, yet they tend to be the less eye-appealing hog in the show ring with droopy ears that cover their eyes and make them the less professional show partner by appearance. Lastly, the Berkshire is a beautifully built hog with decent length and width to accompany it. They are genuinely eye-appealing, but they tend to be the more aggressive, less cooperative show hog when it boils down to temperament. They will get the job done but will likely need extra training to build trust and create a collaborative partnership that will be productive in the ring.

Betty, the purebred Yorkshire

Peggy, the purebred Hampshire.

With all these different breeds to choose from, it is hard to pick just one to take with you into the ring, hoping to be successful. This leads to the idea of producing a crossbred hog. These pigs are unique because using the craft of crossbreeding, one can take qualities of different breeds and generate their own type of pig. My personal favorite cross is a Hamp with a York. Both have the temperate that is desired to be a working partner in the ring, but with the physical qualities of both, they can also be successful in the market class and provide high-quality cuts of meat. When two or more breeds are crossed, these pigs are often called Exotics and get the best traction in the show ring. Additionally, some very interesting colors come out of Exotic litters, including calico, blue, speckled, spotted, and even solid black. When in the show ring, it is not only important to have a well-behaved pig that has a decent build, but you also want one that will grab the judge's eye, which leads me to tip number two.

Some exotic pigs and an example of a blue hog.

Tip 2: Pick a pig with eye appeal

When you are in the show ring, you are not the only one driving a hog, with the judge's attention all on you. There are up to 15 others in the ring with you, sometimes more, all trying to get the judge's attention. It is easy to drown and get swamped by the crowd, lost by the judge's eye. Not only do you have to be resilient to make sure you stay where the judge can see you but picking a pig that stands out can help make sure eyes stay on you. In a show ring of black and white hogs, you want to be the one that is flashy and stands out.

Some of the colors that stand out are blue, calico, and spot. If your pig stands out in color, then it will be easier for the judge to find you in the wave of other pigs, allowing you to rise to the top of their placing.

It is important to pick a pig with an eye-catching color, yet if they don't have the physique to back it up, they will end up doing poorly. The rule of thumb when picking a pig based on its physical appearance is to focus on structure; everything else can be enhanced using correct feedings. Muscle mass can be defined, fat can be added, temperament can be corrected with training, but you cannot fix a structural issue in pigs with simple remedies. The three main structural things to look for are sturdy legs, wide build, and length through the middle. The legs need to be strong enough to support the pig as they grow and get bigger because they start to weigh more and have a build that is difficult to support. Bones should be large because the bigger the bone, the more muscle the bone can support, which translates to more meat to harvest. Moving from the ground up, if the hog has square feet under them and sound legs holding them up, now you want width. The width allows for more muscle mass between shoulder blades and across the chest floor. Bacon is one of the most popular cuts of meat on a pig; it is located on the belly. If the pig is wide and long, they will be able to produce more of that bacon. When it comes to structuring, it is vital that the pig has sound feet and legs, a width that carries from shoulder to rump, and length between shoulder and loin.

Now that you know what to look for when selecting a pig when it comes to eye appeal, you have to learn how to choose the correct sow to produce those show pigs.

Selecting the Sow to Produce the Hogs

Now that the topic of breed, color, and structure have been touched on, we must determine how to get to that point by picking a sow, the big mama who will provide the future show pigs. When picking a sow, one has to be very careful about what one is looking for. These girls need to be resilient and built to last but also have the features one wants to pass down and see in their show stock. This section will talk about the specific qualities to look for when picking a sow.

Tip 3: Temperament is everything

Ever heard the phrase "she's a mama bear"? Female bears are known for being vicious defenders of their cubs. Bears bear the same name as pigs when it comes to a female versus a male, sow, and boar. I don't believe this is without reason because, like the bear version of a sow, pigs can be extremely defensive and vicious towards those interfering and messing with their young. Sows have been known to chase their farmers out of the barn, grabbing a pantleg or even drawing blood in the process.

For this reason, sow temperament is crucial to building a successful breeding operation. When picking a sow, I typically look to breed first (always a York, Hamp, or an exotic. I have at least one of each), but then it boils down to if I would feel safe in the barn with these girls. Sows shouldn't be touchy or overly sensitive to you rubbing them anywhere and everywhere. It is normal for them to be nervous when you first meet them, but after they are used to you, they should be willing with pretty much anything you do. I often test the trust of my sows by rubbing my hands all over their face, over their eyes, and even across their lips and on their nose. If the sow snaps at me or tries to bite, this is often a tell-tale sign that they will not be trusted in the farrowing barn and are not worth keeping.

This is so crucial in a sow because personality is often passed down through litters. When I was first starting my breeding business, I had my first sow, and she was a doll. Very sociable, loved to go on walks and be around people. Out of her first litter, I raised a show barrow (a male pig without testicles) for a county fair that was in September. He was a Hamp crossbred, so he was all black with a white belt. When we were in the show ring, at 90+ degrees outside, he started to overheat. All the other hogs in the ring were white and could regulate their temperature much better than he could.

We were in the final round, so this was his fourth time in the ring for that weekend. Never had he shown signs of unwillingness to work. We had trained; however, he was becoming spent and was ready to be done. The judge had opened the gate heading back to the barns, and if your pig went through the gate, you were done and out of the champion round. He knew where to go. I struggled to keep him away from the gate. He was panting, and with every tap of the whip, he was getting more and more stressed. So as a "hail Mary," I put my whip in my pocket, my right hand on his rump, and my left hand in his mouth, resting between his front and back teeth. Finally, I was able to direct him back to the middle of the ring, with half my hand in his mouth, switching hands when we switched directions. He could have easily taken my hand off. Gotten mad and bit me to get away, but I trusted him not to, and he trusted me to take care of him, guiding him where he needed to go. We continued this for another 5-10 minutes before the heat reached him, and I couldn't deny him access to freedom anymore. He got to a water puddle and collapsed into it immediately to cool off. The judge said that if I had gotten him away from the gate one more time, I would have been the Grand Champion Showman out of sheer will and due to my bond with him. When I got to him after shaking hands with the judge, Tank gave me a look I will never forget. He looked at me with disappointment in his eyes. He was given a job and was unable to fulfill it. His disappointment wasn't in me; it was in himself that he couldn't keep going.

For days after this event, I heard talk around the barn from other showmen, saying they would never have trusted their pig with a hand in its mouth, that they were shocked I would even attempt such a thing. Yet, I knew the temperament of my hog and had confidence in Tank. It is, for this reason, that to this day, I put temperament above all other qualities in a sow.

However, sows are more than their personality. One still needs to have success in mind when they are picking a producer, and that leads me to tip number four.

Tip 4: Selecting the sow with the best physique

Unlike your show pigs, sows need to be built to last. They aren't meant for a 6–8-month lifespan. Instead, they often need to stay productive for up to seven years, having two litters per year. That puts a lot of stress and wear and tear on a sow. So naturally, these girls need to be built differently to withstand the stresses sows face.

The first thing to look at when picking a long-term sow is structure. You want to have legs and feet to support her as she grows, as well as when she gains weight from supporting an 8-12 pig litter when in gestation. Pasterns (like an ankle on a human) are the first thing to break down in pigs, as they can be weak, and if not dieted correctly, pigs can become larger than their feet can support. These need to be strong. Often when looking at pasterns, the shorter the pastern is, the stronger it will be. When pasterns are too long, it puts more pressure on that joint, causing it to break down faster. Pasterns stay supportive when the sow also has square feet that are shaped correctly. Also, having the bigger bone allows the pastern to be stronger than if the legs are skinny or weak in stature.

An example of structurally correct pasterns on a sow.

The next structural factor to pay attention to is the width between hips. When in gestation, piglets grow extremely fast, and when they get to be 3 lbs. or bigger, they get very large. With this being said, the wider the hips are, the easier it is for a sow to have her litter. There have been many times when I have had to assist a sow while they are giving birth by reaching into the birth canal because they couldn't have the babies on their own. When a sow has appropriately sized hips, farrowing goes a lot smoother because they can have them unassisted, leaving you to have more time to attend to the ones already on the ground. Thus, having a sow that has the structure to support the litter and birth is necessary to have a successful breeding operation.

Another factor to consider while picking as sow is determining how many teats she has. Sows often have an even number with the same amount on each side of the belly (7X7 or 6x6). The more nipples they have, the better. The average nipple amount tends to be a total of 12. This means that the sow can support 12 piglets. So, if she has less than that, then the piglets who do not get a teat go hungry. When piglets are young, they are often all feeding at the same time, and they often drink till they are full or they run out of milk in their teat. So, the piglets that do not receive a nipple don't eat that rotation. If this happens too often, the piglet is less likely to survive, or the farmer will have to supplement with milk replacer. Having supply to match the demand for milk is crucial; therefore, it is vital to check for the number of teats; anything less than 12 total could impair the litter's success and growth.

Lastly, the point of a sow is to produce show pigs; thus, she must have desired qualities of a show pig to pass onto her litter. When picking a sow, you aren't going to pick the one with the weakest ham and the narrowest build just because she is a pretty color and acts friendly. Sows need to have show pig features to pass down to their litters. The prime features to watch for that would be ideal in a potential show pig are broad chest floor, wide hips/ham, elongated neck, and correct feet. A lot of the confirmation that sows need to have to be productive, our show pigs also need to possess to be considered quality hogs. The only thing that sows often do not contain that are desired in show hogs is seeing an elongated body. When sows are too long between their hips and shoulder, their muscles are stretched out between this area, so when it comes to farrowing (giving birth to piglets), it becomes more difficult to have babies. When the muscles are closer together, they are more functional for contraction and birthing piglets with ease.

With all this talk about picking the correct sow for your operation, there is a vital part about a sow that impacts how you breed: their heat cycle. This topic leads me to tip number five.

Tip 5: How to track a heat cycle

In order to breed your sow, before you even consider which boar to pick, you must be able to track when she is in heat. A heat cycle is when a pig is ovulating and thus ready to breed. There are two different parts of heat, and it is important to know both. The first is the initial heat. This is when a pig starts to ovulate, but they are not receptive to a boar or to being bred. The signs for this will be swollen or enlarged vulva, milky white discharge, being more mouthy (loud or temperamental), grumpy, etc. It is at this point that you should order your semen. The next part of the heat cycle is when a sow is in standing heat. This will have all the other signs except that when you put pressure on her back, she will perk her ears and tail and stand still for you.

Additionally, you may notice her standing alone and leaning against walls to put pressure on herself when she would normally be coming up to you. This is when she is the most fertile, so it is at this point that you should attempt to breed her. The average heat cycle is about 3-5 days in length, and standing heat can be as short as 12 hours. Therefore, it is crucial to understand how your sow functions and what her heat cycle is like. Sows typically come into heat every 21 days, give or take a day or two. They generally are very regular; however, every hog is different. Before you wish to breed, I recommend letting your sow go through a few cycles to ensure you know her timing and when she is the most fertile. Learn her signs, her behaviors, and her timing. This will help make the breeding process easier and more successful.

After you have picked your sow and determined when she is in heat, you will need to pick a boar to breed her to. In this next section, you will learn how to choose a boar that is complimentary to your sow and how to breed her once you have decided who to breed her to.

Picking the Prime Boar for Your Sow

You have determined what breed you want to produce, analyzed and picked your perfect sow, and tracked her heat cycle, but now you need to find the best boar for your needs. This leads me to tip number six.

Tip 6: Decide Between Live Cover and AI

There are two different ways to breed a sow to produce a litter; live cover and artificial insemination (AI). With live cover, you either pick a boar that someone else has, or you own a boar for yourself to use when needed. AI is when you order semen from a facility from a boar of your choice. The most common way is to AI breed because you don't have to own the boar or house it, and it is also easier on the sows. In addition, boars weigh a lot as they get older, and the bigger they are, the harder it is on your sow during the breeding process. Yet some choose not to use AI because they must deliver the semen themselves into the sow, which can be an uncomfortable experience. So, for those that wish to use a live boar rather than semen in a bottle, tip number seven is for you.

Tip 7: How to House a Boar

Boars are the most destructive type of hog there is. Sows can be destructive simply because they are larger, but boars need a stall or pen that is durable for their size and their destructive nature. So, unless you are going to find a farm and simply borrow their boar, you need to be prepared.

For boars, concrete floors are a must. They are unbreakable for them, and while walking on the cement, their hooves get filed, which helps keep their feet square and in the correct shape to last a lifetime of breeding. If concrete is possible, it is better than wood because pigs can chew through wood, and it will often need to be repaired. If an outdoor area is desired for the boar, using strong metal paneling will be necessary to prevent any escaping or damage to the pen. For all my sows, they do well in stalls that have wooden floors, wooden walls, and a roof over the top. I usually put a metal panel gate that has a wire-filled front. My sows have all done well in these pens, even my most destructive ones, but the boars that I have kept in similar pens have destroyed the flooring and needed something sturdier. For this reason, I don't keep boars anymore because they are difficult to house. For those like me, who would prefer to AI breed, tip number eight is for you.

Tip 8: How to AI breed

The first part of AI breeding is deciding where you are going to order the semen from. There are many different facilities across the country that house boars and sell semen online. Over the past 6+ years of breeding, I have stuck strictly with "Shipley Swine Genetics" for all my pig-related needs; whether it was semen or ordering a bred gilt, Shipley's is my go-to. Yet, I would recommend researching the different facilities to choose the best one for you. I have stuck with Shipley's because not only is it affordable in comparison to others, but they also discount semen each week, they have impeccable customer service, and they have high-quality boars that never disappoint.

Not only have I ordered semen from Shipley's, but I have also ordered gilts that were already bred. The purpose of this is to get a gilt that is already due with babies around the time you want them born. They range in price, and you can even pre-order them to be what you want. Over the years, I have ordered a total of 6 gilts and haven't been disappointed with a single one of them. I bring this up because due to this, I have gotten to know the Shipley family well. There have been times when they call me and help me when I am having issues or questions when it is 10 p.m. where they are. They truly know what it means to have great customer service. I will recommend their service to anyone as much as I can.

Once you have decided where you will get your semen, you must pick a boar. When choosing a boar, you want to look for qualities that complement the sow you have. If she isn't as long, find a boar that is. If she is less structurally sound, pick a boar that is. Other than this, picking a boar is very similar to picking a sow. You want to see those show-pig qualities, and you want to pick one with eye appeal. Pick a boar that not only has the physical qualities you desire but is also the breed you want and will potentially throw the color you wish to see in your litter. Pay attention to the price of the boar in comparison to the other boars. Facilities will often price the boars in accordance with which ones they believe are the better ones to use. The prices can be tell-tale signs in which boar will likely be a better candidate as well. Lastly, each facility should list a section of statistics that goes with that boar. These include the birth date, the litter size if they carry a stress gene, etc. Make sure to look at this, and if you have questions, when you order your semen, ask an employee at the facility to explain it to you. They are often extremely helpful and rich with information. These are all things to think about when picking a boar.

Once you have selected your boar, you should call the facility to order it. You should order at least two, but I would recommend getting three unless you have a sow who is extremely regular and easy to catch while in heat. You also want to make sure that your sow is in standing heat when it arrives because semen doesn't stay good forever. These doses are the number of chances you will have to get her bred. Additionally, you should ask for AI rods. These are the rods that you will use to inseminate the pig. They are hard to find in agricultural stores, so it is always easier to order online since you will be unable to deliver the semen into the sow without them.

When your semen arrives (it should be the next day, semen is considered a priority and is express shipped from wherever you ordered it), it will be in a box that is insulated and has ice packs to regulate the temperature of the semen. When removing it from the box, it is best to do this in a dark room. Direct light, especially sunlight, can kill the semen and ruin it. The temperature needs to be regulated between 59 degrees Fahrenheit and 64 degrees Fahrenheit to keep it alive when storing it. Additionally, the doses that don't get used right away need to be turned twice a day (about 12 hours apart), or else the sperm can drown at the bottom of the container they are in, making it less fertile or potent.

After you have determined your sow is in standing heat, you will give them their first dose of semen. To do this, you will need your AI rod, one container of semen, and optional is lube to help put the AI rod in. AI rods have a small corkscrew end, and the rest is a tube where the semen attaches to the rod. To get the sow ready for breeding, you should sit on her back to put pressure, just like the boar would for live cover. Then, if you wish to put lube on the rod, you can put a small amount on now. Then you will turn the AI rod into the vulva clockwise. It needs to be turned rather than just administered directly because the vaginal canal inside a pig is corkscrewed; thus, one must screw the rod into place. The rod should be aimed toward the back at an angle to ensure the rod does not go into the urinary tract instead of the vaginal canal. Then once you reach a spot where the rod will not go any farther, you will open the other side of the rod and attach the container. Then slightly squeeze the vial to push the semen into the rod and into the sow. Be sure not to squeeze too hard, or it will be too fast, and the semen will come back out of the vulva. If the sow is truly in standing heat, she should start to suck the semen like a vacuum, meaning you barely have to squeeze it at all. After the vial is empty, you can slowly remove the rod to ensure there is no semen left in the rod while doing so. Then be sure to watch the sow for a few minutes afterward to ensure no semen starts to come back out. You will do this again in 12 hours with dose number two, and then in another 12 hours for dose number three if she is still in heat.

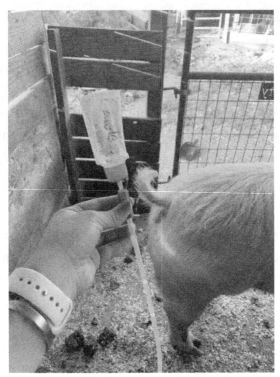

Semen container attached to the end of an AI rod immediately after administering a dose of semen.

Once a sow is bred, it isn't smooth sailing until she gives birth. Pigs are extremely sensitive animals that need to have structure in their lives. Throughout the entire pregnancy (three weeks, three months, and three days; 114 days), you will need to ensure they are on a good diet, have all the vaccinations they need, their pen is maintained, and they are taken care of properly, no matter the season they are in... segueing into our next topic.

Sow Maintenance

Sows need special care, especially when they are bred with a high-quality show litter. One hundred fourteen days from their first dose of semen is when sows typically go into labor, and for those 114 days, the sow needs to be treated as though she is a temple, starting with her diet.

Tip 9: Keep Your Sow on a Strict Diet

A common misconception regarding pigs is that they need to "eat a lot" simply because they are pigs. If given the opportunity, they would eat anything they have access to. Yet, inside that sow, about 12 little piglets grow at an alarming rate, and the more she eats, the bigger they get, the bigger they get, the harder it is for her to have them. Not only this, but the sow needs to be kept in shape as well because if she gets too big, she will be unable to farrow her litter unassisted successfully. To ensure the sow and the precious littles she is carrying stay at an appropriate size, they must be kept on a strict, three-pounds of grain per day diet.

Additionally, if you have access to a feed mill where it is produced, they should be fed "gestation" grain. This is a grain specifically formulated to meet the needs of a pregnant sow. Keeping the amount provided to her per day restricted helps keep the litter at a reasonable size, and prevents her from gaining too much weight, whether that be baby weight or just extra pounds. This should be maintained after she is 21 days bred. Before this point, giving her an extra pound per day would be beneficial to ensure she gets the nutrients needed to take the semen and get bred. At 21 days bred, this is the first sign that she will be having a litter because if she weren't, she would be coming into heat on this day.

Yet a diet is not the only thing that needs to be managed while your sow is bred. They need their required and necessary vaccines to ensure a healthy litter and a healthy sow.

Tip 10: Keep Track of Vaccinations

Similar to people and dogs, pigs need their shots to stay healthy. This is crucial during the time that the sow is bred. One of which is making sure to deworm your sows a few weeks before they farrow. The brand that I prefer is 'Noromectin.' It is an Ivermectin dewormer that is injectable. Other forms of deworming exist, such as oral both by feed or by water, but I have learned that the injectable form is easier to give, cheaper to obtain, and easier to ensure they get the correct amount. All bottles of injections have the dosage and instructions on them. First, it will inform you how much to give in ml based on weight; then it will inform you about giving the injection intramuscularly (in the muscle) or subcutaneously (under the skin); however, most vaccinations, at least in pigs, are intramuscular, which is the easier type of the two.

Another type of injection that is recommended is called 'Farrowsure Gold B". Yet, this vaccination should be given prior to breeding your sow. It is a vaccination that protects against porcine parvovirus, six different strains of leptospirosis, and erysipelas. It is recommended to give a dose 2-4 weeks before breeding and 3-5 weeks before that. Then a booster prior to each breeding. Piglets are extremely fragile, especially when they are in their younger weeks. Thus, having the extra protection to keep them safe from any potential illnesses they may face will ensure you have the most productive litter.

Tip 11: No Matter the Season, Meet the Needs of Your Sow

As I have stated before, pigs as a species are extremely sensitive. Stress is a major concern when raising sows and show stock. Therefore, it is crucial to meet the animal's needs in all seasons throughout the year. In the winter, heat lamps and straw are a must. In each sow pen, I have at least two heat lamps on at a time to keep them warm, especially in below-freezing temperatures.

Additionally, water needs to be kept from freezing in waterers. This can be done using a water heater that is plastic safe. It is crucial to use plastic safe because the type of waterer that I recommend is made of PVC and would melt otherwise. Even in the freezing temperatures, pigs still need a lot of water to maintain their health. Because of this, when it is extra cold, I will give the slightest bit more grain to my sows than I usually do. To explain how minimal the additional grain is, if I give them half a scoop normally per feeding, they will receive about 5/8 -3/4 of a scoop in comparison. This is simply because they burn energy trying to stay warm, so this extra half a scoop per day would be burned off, meaning it will not influence the litter or the sow. Providing the extra grain also helps prevent the sow from becoming stressed and potentially losing her litter due to a lack of calories for the low temperatures. This is why it is crucial to ensure your sow stays warm and has plenty of what she needs in the winter because a sow in shock due to weather change or stressed about temperature could lose her litter.

An example of the waterers I build for all of my hogs. These are made out of PVC and then a gravity water nipple is installed on the end.

The same goes for in the summer, when temperatures are hot as can be. Where I am from, it got up to 113 degrees this last summer. In the barns where I keep my sows, they don't have access to the outside unless I let them out, and they do not have a mudhole, which is their usual way of cooling down in the summer. So, to substitute this cooling strategy they typically use, I install misters in each of the barns to be run during the day. These misters let out enough water to form a pool of water on the floor for them to lay down in and cool off. I also water down their feed with cold water. This ensures hydration, helps cool them down from the inside out and encourages them to eat their food. When the temperature gets too hot for sows in the summer, they could become lethargic, which is no good for a sow, let alone one that has a litter on the way. So alongside misters and watering down food, I also install one box fan per stall to circulate the air and help lower the temperature in the pen. It can be challenging to build a sustainable barn that meets a sow's needs for summer and winter. This leads to stalls with solid walls, but solid walls keep heat in and become ovens. So having a box fan to push and pull air in and out can help lower the temperature, create an artificial breeze, and make life a little more enjoyable for your sow. Lastly, regarding summer maintenance, I am led to reoccurring, tip number 12.

Tip 12: Go Natural

If there is one thing that I have learned while raising pigs, it is that not all things that come from a box are what your pig needs. Over the last six years, I have had time to research and go through the process of trial and error to determine what is best for my hogs, and I have learned that natural is best. One of my favorite summertime hacks for raising hogs is incorporating cucumbers into their regular diet. They are practically calorie-less, so there is no worry about overfeeding a sow on cucumbers, and they have cooling properties. Implementing these into the sow's everyday summer diet helps cool them from the inside out, making the hot days more tolerable for them. They are also mostly made of water, so there are hydration keys to them as well. The same goes for other fruits and vegetables that could help regulate temperature or are mostly made of water, such as watermelon. Giving garden or dinner scraps similar to these to your sow can make a world of difference if they make it through the summer, stress-free.

Chapter Review:

- Know the most common breeds of pigs; Duroc, Hampshire, Yorkshire, and Berkshire.
- Understand that temperament is the most important thing in all pigs.
- Know how to pick out a sow based on eye appeal regarding structure and physique.
- Learned how to track a heat cycle in your sow.
- Picking a quality boar; know to look for the features that would complement your sow.
- Decide between AI and live cover for breeding.
- Learn how to AI breed if that is the route you choose.
- Know how to house and maintain a sow and potentially a boar, and keep them healthy.

Chapter 2: Taking Care of a Farrowing Sow

At this point, we have talked about all the details that go into picking a sow, picking a boar, and getting that sow bred. Now that she is bred, it's time to start thinking about how to take care of her during the days leading up to farrowing, during labor, and while she is giving birth.

How to Prepare

Getting ready for farrowing is stressful for both the sow and you. However, being prepared with a few key tips can make everything run smoothly and keep your sow in good shape for delivering the future show ring champions.

Tip 13: Setting up your farrowing barn

No matter the season, piglets need to stay warm. When they are young, this is extra crucial to their health. Therefore, it is important to have power at your barn. Power is needed whether you use extension cords from other outlets or have sockets in the barn. I typically have two heat lamps for the piglets in the summer, and I also have a fan plugged in to keep mom cool when it is extremely hot. Yet, I always have three heat lamps plugged in in the winter. One for mom and two for the babies, and then I have to make sure I also have a water heater for mom's waterer. Each of my farrowing barns has a four-outlet electrical unit for anything that I would need to plug in. With first-time moms, I spend the night with them for the first night the piglets are on the ground, so this is also helpful for those who need a charging station for electronic devices; not a necessity in that sense, but definitely handy.

As one can imagine, sows are a lot bigger than the babies they have. The piglets are usually around three pounds, but the moms are typically over 300 pounds, making them much larger than the littles they produce. Thus, the farrowing barn needs to be a place where the piglets can be safe.

In my barn, I use farrowing crates. Farrowing crates are metal structures like cages that you put the sow in so that she cannot turn around. She can stand up, lay down on either side, and has access to her food and water, but she is unable to go anywhere unless the crate is open. I started to implement this because, with my first sow, we did not have one. We built bumper walls so that the piglets had somewhere they could go to get away from mom and lay with the heat lamp, but mom was able to turn around go anywhere she pleased. This posed a problem when it came time for her to farrow. When she was having her litter, any time one squeaked or made a noise, she would jump up and turn around to check on them. This was a great motherly instinct, but when she did this, she was so hyper-focused on the upset piglet that any of the other ones she had on the ground that were in her way got trampled. She had a total of 14 in that litter, but only nine survived because all the ones she stepped on had internal bleeding and injuries that could not be fixed.

Additionally, there were more places to lay down without the crate, so it was easier for her to lay on her piglets. The very next year, I bought myself two farrowing crates to prevent this from happening again. Piglets need to have somewhere to get away from mom if they want to. This is where you put their feed that mom can't have, their heat lamps that mom can't get to, and where they typically sleep where they are safely away from the danger of being stepped or laid on. For all these reasons, I would have a farrowing crate in my list of necessities in the farrowing barn.

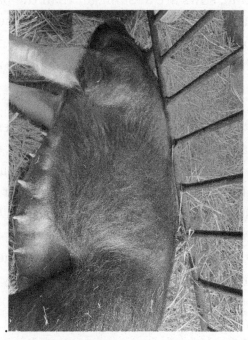

An Exotic sow getting ready to labor in her farrowing crate.

However, even if you have a farrowing crate in your barn, unless you leave your sow in it for the entire three weeks that the piglets are nursing, you will need to have a plan to implement some bumper walls. I typically leave mom in the crate until the litter is one week old (after I castrate) and then pull it out. This is beneficial for the mom because it allows her to walk around, stretch her legs, and make them more comfortable. At this point, piglets are also more aware of where mom's feet are and know where not to be. Yet I still put bumper walls up so that the piglets have somewhere they can go to eat their "nursery" grain and have their own waterer. Be prepared to build these and put them in when the crate gets pulled out.

Along with the farrowing crate, there is a list of other necessities that should be in the barn with you when your sow farrows her litter. This leads me to tip number 14.

Tip 14: Get what you need, prior to needing it

One of the most stressful situations to be in is needing an injection or a tool in the middle of farrowing and not having it. Therefore, one of my biggest tips is to make sure you get all the things you need before the farrowing begins. My list of must-haves when in the farrowing barn include:

- Tooth clippers (for piglets)
- Oxytocin (this is a prescription drug and will need to be retrieved by a vet)
- Ear notchers (for identification)
- Iodine (for open wounds, prevents infection)
- Pedialyte (for sow hydration)
- Scours syrup (for piglets)
- Lube (in case farrowing assistance is needed)
- Gloves (in case farrowing assistance is needed)
- A wormer (for piglets)
- Estrumate (this is also a prescription drug, so visit your vet for this item)
- LA 200 (for infections or illness in sows and piglets)
- Vitamin B (injection for piglets)
- Floss (for tying umbilical cords)
- Scissors (for cutting umbilical cords)
- Lots of straw (for warmth, comfort, and cleanliness)
- Heat lamps or heat mats (to keep sow and piglets warm)
- Shop towels (for wiping off and cleaning piglets)
- 18 GA needles (for injections)
- 20 GA needles (for injections)
- 5ml syringes (for injections)
- Sow laxative

- Nasal bulb
- Thermometer
- Wet Chalk Marker

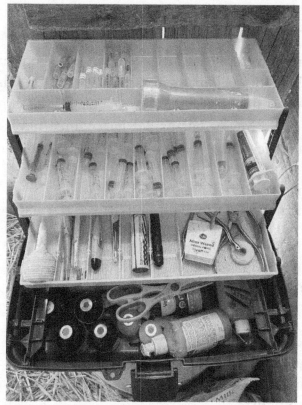

Fishing tackle box converted into a tool kit for medical needs.

Each of these items has a specific purpose in the farrowing barn for the needs of the sow and the litter. Therefore, I would recommend that anyone getting ready to have a sow farrow a litter obtain all of these things for their kit before farrowing begins.

With this list in mind, now comes the topic of what to use all of these tools for and when to use them. This leads to the next tip of Chapter 2.

Tip 15: Make sure your sow is ready to farrow

Labor is a very exhausting and strenuous process for any being. In order to ensure that everything goes smoothly, it is important to prepare your sow for farrowing. There are a few things that need to happen in the days leading up to farrowing.

First, she will need to be wormed a week before going into labor. This is another reason why it is crucial to know when your sow is due because, throughout their gestation, they need certain treatments. This worming will help to cover mom and give the piglets some immunity in their first couple weeks in the world.

Second, mom will need to be cleaned, a crate needs to be put into her barn, and she needs to be crated a few days before she farrows. It is important that she gets cleaned to ensure there is nothing on her that she could potentially give to the piglets when they are at their most sensitive age. Additionally, putting a sow in her crate a few days before she is due is helpful, especially for first-time moms. They need to get used to and acquainted with the crate before going through the stressful experience of farrowing. It is also at this point where you need to make sure they get a laxative for the few days leading up to farrowing. It is easier for them to give birth to the litter if there isn't a stool obstructing the birthing canal. Additionally, you want your sow to be as comfortable as possible while giving birth, and that includes preventing them from having constipation.

Mineral oil that I use as a mild laxative for my sows.

Once your sow is comfortable in her farrowing environment, she has her laxative, and all your tools are acquired, you are ready for her to farrow. Tip 16 helps you to determine when it is "go time," and your sow should start to farrow her litter.

Tip 16: Know the signs of pre-labor

As stated before, sows are in gestation for 114 days from their first dose of semen. Sows are typically very regular and stick to this due date. Generally, it is okay to let them go past their due date up until 114 days from the final dose they received, but any further than that, it is recommended that you induce your sow. This is because, as stated before, piglets grow at an astronomical rate. Any extra time past their due date that they spend in the womb rather than on the ground, they gain size and weight. Anything bigger than a three-pound piglet at birth is large and typically too big for a first-time mom to have on her own. For this reason, we usually induce the sows when they go past their due date, using Estrumate.

Estrumate is a drug used in cows to cause an artificial abortion. Farmers may use it if a cow was too young when they got bred, or they got into the wrong herd, or maybe it is strictly for the cow's health. Whatever the reason may be, this drug was created for that purpose and, when dosed correctly, can be used to induce a sow into labor. A dosage for Estrumate is typically 1ml. This should be given intramuscularly, and I usually do so in the rear, where it is soft. After this is given, she should go into labor 12 hours later.

Yet, how will you know when your sow is in labor? One thing is for certain, try to understand your sow's behaviors. When a sow is getting ready for labor, she starts to go through changes, both physically and behaviorally. Regarding behavior, she will start to nest. Nesting is when an animal prepares for labor by making a bed for themselves out of bedding. You can tell your sow is starting to nest when she is maneuvering the straw, trying to build a bed around herself, especially around her birthing region. Of course, she will want to make herself as comfortable as she can, but she also will want to ensure that when she has her babies, they have a soft landing and lots of straw to protect them when they are born.

Another behavior you may notice is your sow may become lethargic. She may start to eat less food because she knows she will need to be ready to give birth. Additionally, it is hard to be hungry when you're uncomfortable. Another thing you may notice in your sow is that she may become grumpy or temperamental. It is hard to gauge how your sow will respond to being in labor. Some of them take it well; others may not react well to it. If you notice a sudden mood change with your sow, you can expect to see her go into labor soon.

There are a few physical changes you may notice about your sow as well. One of which is the month or so leading up to farrowing, her teats will start to swell. Her teats will fill with milk about a week before, and her belly will drop. This sign gives more of a heads-up because it doesn't happen overnight or the day before labor; it happens a few days at the least. If you notice this happening, you can start to get in the mindset and prepare for your litter.

Additionally, in the days leading up to farrowing, your sow will start to soften around her tailhead and vulva. The ligaments that keep everything tight in that region will begin to soften and deteriorate, making it easier for the sow to have her babies. Therefore, it would be a good idea to know what the tailhead feels like before your sow starts to soften. That way, you can determine when the softening process begins. Generally, when the ligaments are completely soft, you will be able to press around the tail head with ease, and the tail will feel very loose. At this point, it will be within a couple of days or hours that labor begins.

Sow that is very bred and starting to bag up with milk leading up to her due date.

All these signs above are about the behaviors and physical changes leading up to labor and how to prepare for it. However, there are also signs to look for that will tell you when your sow is in labor. For this, you will need to read tip number 17.

Tip 17: Know the signs of active labor

A sow's labor goes very quickly. Therefore, it is important to know and understand the sure signs of labor to ensure you are there to assist if needed.

The first big sign that labor is near or already upon you is if you can get milk out of your sow's teats. You should check for this at least twice a day, for each of the days leading up to farrowing. You can do this by lightly squeezing each teat to see if you get any milk out of one. Make sure to check each one, because milk will come in at different times for each teat. Once you get some milk out, even just a drop, it is safe to assume that your sow will be in active labor within 12 hours.

When your sow is in active labor, you will notice she is lying on her side and having contractions. Contractions in pigs are noticeable when they lift their leg and grunt or hold their breath. These contractions are typically paired with pushing, which is another sign that she is in active labor. You may also notice a discharge coming out of her vulva. If you notice a large amount of discharge/liquid come out at once, that indicates that her water has broken, and she should have the first baby within a couple of hours, if not in 30 min.

With all these different signs, your sow is going to be extremely uncomfortable, and she is going to be in pain. So, while she is in labor, it is important to ensure she feels safe and as comfortable as possible.

A sow in active labor, laying in the typical birthing position, in her nested farrowing crate. Looking at her teats, one can tell that she is in full milk.

Tip 18: Sows needs come first

When your sow is in labor, she is contracting, pushing, grunting out a whole litter of pigs, and that is not easy work. But, as her farmer, it is your job to ensure that you keep her comfortable and meet her needs.

When I have a laboring sow, I try to be there for the entire process (I have had one sow who is very deliberate about being on her own. I showed up one morning, and she had six out of seven of her piglets from the litter in the middle of the night, before I even expected her to be in active labor) because there are so many things that could go wrong, and you never know when you may need to assist your sow. Additionally, I like to be there for the process so that I can assist my sow as much as possible. Some of the things I make sure to have to help my sow are:

- A bucket of water for drinking
- Blankets (if it is winter and she starts to shake)
- Her favorite snack (peaches, apples, treats, etc.)
- Wet towels (strictly for summertime if overheating occurs)

In between contractions, I will check and see if she wants a drink of water by holding the bucket by her nose. This helps her to keep hydrated. The blankets are strictly for wintertime if there is not enough heat and she needs warmth, and the towels are strictly for summer if she starts to overheat. The snack, however, is based on a sow that I had a few years ago, who while she was in labor with her first litter, I was staying up with her, it was well past midnight, and I had some snacks for myself. Among these snacks included a jar of peaches I was eating. At one point, while I was eating the peaches, she had a break in contractions, smelled the peaches, and was trying to grab one while she was still lying down. I held one over her nose, and she took it. This went on a few more times throughout the night. I like to think of the snacks as an energy boost, and it definitely made Bree happy, being able to eat some peaches in between her contractions.

Another thing that you can do to keep your sow comfortable is to help speed things along. By rubbing the sow's tummy, you help produce oxytocin, which helps make labor move faster and get the piglets out. Additionally, if your sow has been in labor for a few hours and there looks to be no progress, you can get her up and out of the crate to take her for a short walk around. Just like in people, walking or moving helps to get the process going faster if you notice that your sow is getting tired of laboring.

This part of the farrowing process can take a few hours; contracting, pushing, breathing, waiting. It truly is a waiting game. However, once that first piglet comes out, things pick up, and it is crucial that you are prepared for when that first hog hits the ground.

Once the Pigs Hit the Ground

After your sow has been laboring for a few hours, you will notice a change in her pushing. She will be grunting more, the leg on the opposite side from where she is laying will be used as leverage for a good push, and you will notice that the contractions are longer. If you wish to see if your sow is dilated, you can glove and lube up, and if your hand can go past your forearm, she is likely ready for the first one to come out. Soon after she is dilated, you will notice a bulge around her vulva, and that is the first piglet coming out. Hopefully, it should be coming out face first, but if it is the other way around, it should be okay as long as it gets out quickly. Now though, you need to know what to do when that little bulge appears, indicating the arrival of piglet number one.

Tip 19: Be ready to catch them

Unlike with other species, I have noticed that piglets quite literally shoot out of the vulva. When I am with my laboring sow, I try to make camp by her rear region to ensure I am present when the piglets come out. When a piglet comes out, you will need to be ready with shop towels to dry and clean the piglet off, a nasal bulb to get the mucus out of the nose and mouth, floss, and scissors for the umbilical cord, and your ear notching and tooth clipping tools.

When the piglet comes out, grab your shop towels and wipe the piglet off. Make sure to start at the face while wiping them off to let the piglet breathe. Then if you are still having trouble getting all of it, you can put your finger in the piglet's mouth to scoop out the liquid, or you can use the nasal bulb to suck it out after you have removed as much as you can. Next, hold the pig upside down and gently shake them to encourage the remaining liquid to exit the mouth. Do this while patting and rubbing the side of the piglet until they make some noise; either a grunt or a squeak will suffice. Then, while the piglet is in your hands, you can begin to "process" them. I call it processing because it is the routine or process that I do with each litter of pigs I have ever raised. Starting my process, I always ear notch for identification on pigs. This leads me to tip number 20.

Tip 20: Used Identification

The most common form of identification in pigs today is ear notching. To do this, one needs the ear notching tool. Each ear has a different purpose, and some use it differently. Since I do not have a large operation with only four sows, I use the left ear on the pig as the sow number. When I only had one sow, I used this as the litter number for that sow. The right ear is used as the number the pig is in the litter. So the first piglet born will have the number one notched in their right ear. Each part of the ear represents a different number as well. If you are looking at the ear from the top, the bottom of the ear represents one. Then the top half of the ear is three. The inside of the ear (on the side where the ears face each other) at the top is nine, the bottom is 18, and the very tip, if needed, is 81. This orientation is the same on both ears. Please note this is the way that I notch the ears for my pigs; however, some

43

other operations may use a different ear notching orientation to identify their pigs. This being said, the numbers always stay the same, but some places switch the ears where the left side is the pig number, and the right is the sow or litter number, for example. Yet the numbers always go 1, 3, 9, 27, 81, no matter which ears the facility uses for which identification key.

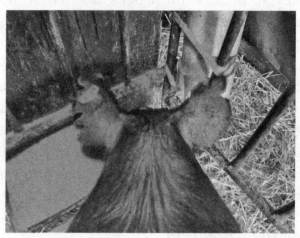

Example of a sow with notched ears. Numbers represent - left is 8 and right is 39

I recommend using identification when raising pigs because if you have multiple sows and the piglets end up being together, or you have an entire litter that looks extremely similar, you can use the ear notches to determine which pig is which. This is especially helpful when selling piglets because the buyer can pick their pig and keep track; you can write down the ear notches corresponding to the pig they pick. Due to this, when the buyer is picking up their pig, there will be no confusion about which pig they picked.

To ear notch, determine which orientation you wish to utilize, notch the ears for the piglet and spray with iodine to prevent infection. Be sure to go deep enough while notching to ensure the notch doesn't close completely, making it useless when they are older. However, you don't have to go super deep, so just be aware of how far you notch. Also, I do this at a young age to make sure I keep the order correct, and it is also less traumatic for the piglet at this age because they forget it right away.

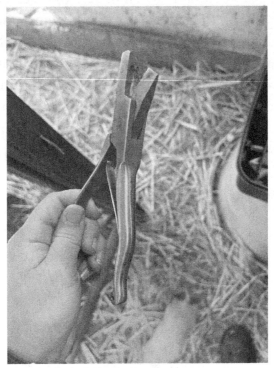

Ear notching tool.

Now that the pig has ear notches for identification, there are two other parts of the process to do before you can put the piglet down to find a teat, leading to tip number 21.

Tip 21: Clip teeth; your sow will thank you

Unlike some species of animals, pigs are born with "eye teeth." These teeth are dagger-sharp and very painful if an unwanted appendage gets caught in them. So once a piglet is born, I make sure to clip these teeth using the tooth nippers. To do this, I lay the piglet on their back in my lap. Then, using my left hand (I am right-handed), I put my thumb in their mouth crossways to keep it open. Then using my other hand, I clip the teeth short enough that they lose their point. They should have four sets that need to be cut, two on the top and two on the bottom. This is extremely important to do for two different reasons. One, it is better for the sow because, with the teeth, the piglets would be tearing up her teats and make it hard for her to nurse them. Two, if these are not clipped, the teeth would continue to grow throughout their lives and become tusks in the future. Show pigs should never have tusks, and if the pig is used as a breeding boar or sow, they should never have tusks either. So, it is the norm to do this with each litter. Some places wait till they are older, but for the first reason I mentioned, and to be less traumatic on the piglets, I do it when they are fresh out of the womb.

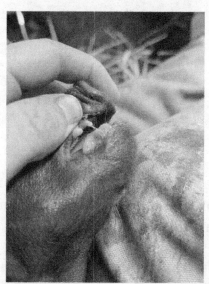

This is an image of freshly born piglet teeth before they are cut. There are pairs of teeth like this on the top and bottom in the mouth and on each side, making eight teeth in total that need to be cut.

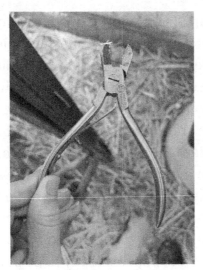
Tooth nipper tool.

Once the teeth are clipped, and the pig is identified, the last part of the process for a freshly born pig is to tie off and cut the umbilical cord.

Tip 22: The umbilical cord has to go

When a piglet is born, typically, the umbilical cord detaches naturally from the mom on its own. When your pig(s) are born, if it does not detach on its own, do not yank it, gently pull on the cord until it breaks free. Piglets do this naturally when they are born because they typically get right up and start moving around, and because of the tension from them moving away from the vulva, the umbilical cord breaks loose. However, when it does so, the cord is extremely long and is easy to step on. When the cord is this long, it gets wrapped around legs, dragged on the ground, and is a huge hassle for the piglets. So, I tie and cut my umbilical cords with floss and scissors.

Similarly, with cutting teeth, I lay the piglet in my lap on their back to have easy access to their cord. Then using a piece of floss that is approximately the length of my hand, I tie it around once, then wrap it around a second time and tie two knots in the floss. I do this approximately an inch away from the pig's belly. When you pull it tight, make sure the knot is tight enough to cut off the blood flow but not too tight where the cord gets cut through. The umbilical cord can be a fragile thing under pressure, so be sure to keep the floss at the right tension. Then once it is tied, I use the scissors to cut off the excess umbilical cord, about half an inch away from the floss. After cutting it, I make sure the cord is not bleeding, spray it with iodine, and then the piglet is ready to be put down to test out their legs. If the cord is still bleeding, you can hold pressure on it with a shop towel, or you can attempt to tie another time that is tighter using a new piece of floss. I have done both to get the cord to stop bleeding, and both are effective. It is imperative that the cord stops bleeding, though, because the piglet can lose too much blood from the umbilical cord.

Example of how to tie the umbilical cord at the correct length away from the piglet and what it should look like if the knot is tight enough.

Once the cord is removed, and the piglet is completely processed, it is ready to start nursing on a teat.

Tip 23: Always help your piglet find and figure out how to nurse

Piglets have incredible instincts when it comes to nursing and finding their way to the teat, but I always take the piglets to a teat and help them learn how to nurse. As I have stated before, I have a sow that is completely capable of having a litter on her own when I am not there, and when I arrived after she birthed the litter, all the piglets were already nursing and had figured out how it worked. Yet, to give them a jumpstart, I always put the teat in the piglet's mouth and gently squeeze their mouth open and shut, simulating the nursing a pig would do on their own. After doing this a few times, the piglet should taste the milk and start to nurse on their own. If the piglet does not begin nursing right away, don't get worried just yet. Sometimes they need to rest after being born and will go to sleep. I recommend that the piglets nurse within an hour of being born to get the colostrum (the first milk that is necessary for a young animal's survival), but letting them rest once they are born can give them the energy needed to get to nursing.

Freshly born piglet latched onto the teat for the first time.

Additionally, you should show the piglet to go where the heat lamps are. The lamps and mom will be their prime source of warmth, so putting the piglet under the heat lamp after they are done nursing will show them where they are safe and can be warm. This also helps keep the piglets away from mom's feet while she is laboring, in case she starts waving them around and accidentally hurts one of the piglets. You will likely be preoccupied with new piglets as they arrive. You will be unable to keep a close eye on the others to keep them safe, so make sure you show the piglets where they can go to get away from mom.

Newborn litter of piglets in a puddle under the warm heat lamps.

After the first piglet is born, things start to pick up and move a lot quicker. Therefore, it is important to understand what comes next and what to expect.

Tip 24: Keep an eye on the clock

As I have stated before, sows are very regular, which carries over into their laboring experience. After the first piglet, you can expect number two in about 45 min to an hour. With each piglet, follow the same process as stated before in the previous tips. After about four piglets, your sow should be getting ready to pass her first placenta. Now you may be wondering why I said "first placenta" when shouldn't they have only one? Well, pigs are extremely unique and interesting. When a sow is bred, she can have quite a few placentas, depending on how many piglets she farrows. Each placenta has up to five piglets in them but typically has an even number because sows usually have an even number of piglets in the litter. If the sow passes the first placenta earlier than four or later than four, it is not time to be alarmed. Each sow is different, but you can assume that once she passes one placenta, she will have a longer period of time between the latest piglet and the next one. After a placenta is passed, the piglets in the next placenta need to break free from the one they are currently in, so it is not unusual for a sow to take an hour and a half to two hours till she has the next piglet.

It's about an hour between each piglet, and it's about two hours after a placenta that she has another, so how do you know when you can stop worrying, and you know when she is done? How will you know which placenta or which piglet is the last one? There is a larger sac called the "afterbirth" that a sow will pass when she is completely done with having her piglets. You will be able to tell the difference between a placenta and afterbirth because afterbirth is darker in color, and it is also larger. The afterbirth is the uterine lining that holds all of the piglets and all of the placentas in the uterus. This is why it is larger because it has to house the entire litter, not just a portion of it. Additionally, it is a darker color because it is deeper in nutrients and blood because it was directly connected to the uterus and distributed everything the litter needed to each of the individual placentas. Once the sow has this, it is safe to assume that she is done with her litter.

Not long after she has the afterbirth, your sow should get up and start to go to the bathroom, eat food, and drink water. All of these are signs that she is done laboring and ready to recover.

These last few tips made farrowing seem like it is down to a science and extremely predictable, but that is not always the case. Sometimes things can go wrong very quickly, and due to this, it is vital for the health and safety of the sow and her litter that you know when to intervene and assist.

Tip 25: Know when to intervene and assist your sow

It can be very easy to tell when something is wrong while farrowing because sows are so regular while laboring. If you notice she hasn't had a piglet yet and her water broke a while ago, she is pushing extremely hard but seems to be making no progress, she is shaking, or if it's been longer than one hour since her last piglet, it may be the time to intervene and help her out.

In the list of tools that I have for my farrowing barn, I always make sure that I have gloves and lube, as well as LA 200. I have all these things in case I need to help my sow in a time of need where the health of her litter or her own health is at stake. My first step is always checking her vaginal canal. I do this by putting on a glove (I use the shoulder-length ones) and putting a generous amount of lube on the glove. Then, shaping my hand like a cone, I insert my hand into the vulva. If it cannot go any farther than my wrist, it is likely that she just isn't dilated yet, but this should only be the case if she hasn't broken her water, and especially not if she has already had some piglets. If you cannot go any farther than your wrist, but she is obviously dilated, feel the blockage, as it could be a piglet stuck in the canal. If you feel legs, loop your fingers between two of them, and pull gently while mom pushes. If you feel a head, open the mouth, put your thumb inside the mouth, gently pinching the bottom jaw, and pull as mom pushes. It is crucial that you only pull while mom pushes, or else this could put excess strain on her and make things worse. Be patient and work with her to get the piglet out. Piglets get stuck like this when they are too large for the mom to push out on her own, or she has been laboring for too long, and she is too tired to put enough effort into pushing.

If you do not meet a blockage, continue into the canal until you are shoulder deep. If you still find no piglets along the way to this point, then it is safe to say she doesn't have any in the birthing canal, and you can take out your arm. Always go to this length to ensure there are no piglets stuck because there is a possibility they are stuck at the pelvis, which is approximately shoulder deep. I have had a litter where two of the piglets got their legs stuck on the pelvis of the sow and were unable to come out. I had to go shoulder-deep into the sow and maneuver their legs in a way that would allow them to come out. If I had not checked her, the piglets would have died, and the sow could have gotten a life-threatening infection. Therefore, I always check my sows if they are taking too long. Because the longer the piglet is in the birthing canal, especially if they are breached (facing backward, legs first), the chances of them surviving drop drastically. This also puts excess stress on your sow, making it more difficult for her to labor properly.

If you find a blockage that is not a piglet along the way, it could be a placenta or the afterbirth. Do not grab it and pull it out. It is important that she has this on her own. Pulling on either of these could damage the uterus and seriously impair your sow's health.

When you take your hand out, give your sow a dose of LA 200 as directed on the bottle in the rear. I give this to prevent her from getting any type of infection from me going through the intrusive act of checking her. If she hasn't had any piglets and it has been a while since her water broke, you can also give her a .5ml dose of Oxytocin. Oxytocin will strengthen the contractions, helping get the piglets into the canal. Never give a dose of oxytocin without checking if a piglet is in the canal. If there is one in there while you give a dose of oxytocin, the contractions in the birthing canal will be too strong for the piglet, and it could be in distress. However, if you think you are just waiting on the after birth, using Oxytocin is unnecessary because that will come on its own time and doesn't need to be rushed.

With all of the information listed above, there is still a situation where checking and pulling out a piglet if it is stuck in the canal isn't enough. There are times when the piglet is too large to remove simply by pulling, and a C-section is needed. At this point, it is crucial to have a vet on call.

Tip 26: Have a vet on speed dial

Sometimes, no matter how structurally correct your sow is, or even if you kept her on a strict diet to prevent the piglets and her from getting too large, her internal structure isn't wide enough to have babies, or the piglets simply became too large for her to have on her own. So if you have been spending too long trying to get out one piglet, or the pelvis is too small for you to get your hand into, it may be time to call a vet to perform a C-section. I have personally never had to do this, and I believe part of that attributes to the company that I purchase pigs and semen from, but it is still something that happens, and I have known people who have had to do it. So, for this reason, you should have a vet that you trust, that you can call in time of need to come out to the farm and perform this surgery.

Some people would say you don't need to call the vet, just take care of it yourself, but with those individuals, the sow never survives, and you have a whole litter of bottle babies, so I would never recommend taking matters into your own hands unless absolutely necessary. Depending on how it plays out, your sow may be able to breed again in the future (that is, of course, if it is not an internal structure issue), and it is always better for the litter to have their mom than it is for them to have a bottle instead. It doesn't happen often, but make sure you are prepared with a trustworthy vet in case it is necessary.

Chapter Review:

- Collect your list of tools before you need them so that you are prepared.
- Set up your farrowing barn appropriately, with a farrowing crate, waterer, heat lamps, and bumper walls.
- Know the physical and behavioral signs of labor in your sow
- Know the signs of active labor in your sow and how to keep her comfortable in all seasons.
- Know how to process a piglet once it is born by getting them to breathe, notching ears, clipping teeth, and tying their umbilical cord before they go to nursing.
- Know when to intervene and assist your sow in a time of struggle or need. Don't be afraid to check her and assist with stuck piglets.
- Keep a close eye on piglet and sow health while farrowing to ensure everyone is successful in the farrowing experience.
- Be able to identify placenta from afterbirth and know when your sow is done having her litter.

Chapter 3: Piglets - Week One to Week Four

In this chapter, we will be discussing everything that goes into getting your litter ready to become show trainees and go out into the world to their new homes. From vaccinations to castrating to weaning, we will cover everything you need to know to get your piglet from day one all the way to week four.

Week One for Your Litter

The first day that your piglets are on the ground is one of the most crucial ones. It is when you start to notice their physical features if they are thriving or struggling and when your attention to detail may be the most critical. In this section, I will guide you by ensuring your litter is given the best chance for survival in a world where they are the most sensitive being.

Tip 27: Advertise your litter to showmen

Your litter is on the ground; you are no longer are counting eggs before your chickens hatch; you now have a head count. Although it is helpful to advertise that you will have a litter in the future, now that you have a number from that litter that will be available, it is helpful to start creating your sell list and contacting anyone you can think of to sell these pigs. I usually do this by advertising on Facebook, in Facebook groups, or even by contacting FFA and 4H groups to see if any showmen will need hogs. Be prepared to provide them with a date they will be ready to go and how much you will be charging. Piglets are ready to go to their new homes one week after they are weaned. I wean at three weeks, but some places wean at four weeks. I wean earlier because it gets them off the property sooner and allows the showmen to start working with their piglets sooner. Additionally, it also makes life easier for the sow, so make sure you decide when you will be weaning, count a week after that and be ready to provide a price for your piglets.

To determine price, a good way to figure out what is reasonable would be to research how much show pigs are going for in your area and fall somewhere in that ballpark. Show pigs go for a much higher price than meat pigs do, so make sure you don't low-ball your hogs. I typically sell my show pigs from $250-$300 per hog. The sows are high quality, semen isn't cheap, and you must consider all the labor you have put into the litter as well. Be sure to consider the time of year, whether it is during a time when shows are most popular or if it is in the off-season. In my area, shows that happen in the spring are less common, so the litters that I have born in the fall are cheaper since not many people go, but in the spring when my litters are for fairs in the fall, the demand is high, because each group has about 10-20 pigs that they need. This is when you will find people willing to pay for what the piglets are worth.

Contacting FFA and 4H groups is the most effective way that you will be able to sell your litter because you will be directly contacting the source of your showmen. Unless you have connections built up already, this is a great way to get started and make it easier for you down the road when you are selling the pigs.

Also, when you are finding buyers, make sure to create a buyer list in order of commitment and inform them that you will be collecting a down payment to hold their spot. The buyers will be able to pick pigs in the order that they commit, allowing them to select the more desirable pigs from the litter. This will make you a more reputable breeder and ensure that everyone picks in fair order.

Pigs are extremely sensitive to elements and the world around them, especially at a young age. This leads us to the next tip regarding how you can ensure your litter's success from day one.

Tip 28: Take notes on your litter's improvement

There is a saying that goes around that states "If you have livestock...you have deadstock". This saying means that if you are a farmer and raise livestock, no matter what kind, you will always have ones that don't make it. While this is true, and I have faced it myself, there are things that you can do to ensure your litter survives, each and every one of them.

On day one, each piglet should be up and walking around and nursing on their own frequently. If you notice one hangs behind in the heat lamp when the others go to nurse (if you remember, piglets always feed together at the same time), there may be an issue. First, take their temperature to see if they may have an infection of some sort. Pigs' normal temperature is 102.6; if it is 103.0, then they have a fever, and it would be beneficial to give them a dose of LA 200 as directed on the bottle. However, if they do not have a fever, they may simply be weaker piglets. If this is the case, walk the piglet over to a teat, and protect them while they nurse. Just like when they are just born, put their mouth on the teat and gently squeeze their mouth to simulate nursing. If there are piglets who are this way, use a wet chalk marker (you can find them at any feed store in the identification section) and put a stripe on the ones who need close attention. Lack of nursing can very quickly turn south if not handled, so it is important that you keep a close eye on those pigs throughout the first week especially. This piglet or piglets should be your priority.

All babies should be nursing at the same time.

With weak piglets, sometimes you must intervene to better their chances of survival by using a milk replacer, which leads me to the next tip.

Tip 29: Milk replacer

Not only is the pig as a whole a sensitive being, but their stomachs are extremely sensitive at a young age. For this reason, they should only be fed one of two different types of milk supplements.

1. If you can find a <u>pig milk replacer,</u> this is best. It is created and formulated specifically for pigs and is the best option for them, for it is less likely to upset their stomach, and it will give them the nutrients they need. Unfortunately, this is not a commonly stocked milk replacer at most feed stores, so it will most likely need to be ordered online from a livestock website such as "Valley Vet Supply."

2. If you cannot find the pig milk replacer or cannot get it in time, your other option is to get a goat milk replacer, or even better, see if you can get some raw goat's milk. Never use a "multispecies" milk replacer on piglets. Their stomachs cannot handle it, and it could kill them. Before I was aware of the consequences, I used this milk replacer on a weak pig, and the effects were fatal. Goat milk is the closest in comparison to pig milk. Especially if you can get raw goat's milk, it will be the best alternative for your pig or piglets if nursing is an issue for them.

A feed pan full of colostrum milk replacer was used with a litter that had some extremely small piglets.

Dairy goats we keep on the property to produce milk for litters and be companions to the pigs.

If your piglet is in the first day or so of their life and is being put onto milk replacer, it would be in their best interest to also get a colostrum supplement of some kind to ensure that they get what they need. Colostrum is the first milk that all mammals produce for their young, and it is nutrient-dense to give them a jumpstart and the best opportunity for survival. But, again, it would be best to give this to a piglet within the first 48 hours if you are bottle feeding this young, just in case they didn't get enough from mom.

While bottle feeding, I often use a baby bottle from the store. It is best to keep it level with the piglet while eating. If a piglet is nursing on mom, they are standing on their legs and have their head semi-level with the teat. So instead of turning them on their back as you would a child, keep the bottle level with the piglet's head. If you don't do this, it is possible that the milk could get into the lungs, and the piglet could drown or have other complications that could make matters worse. Use the directions on the bag to create the ration for the piglet and feed them every two hours or so. The bottle will not smell like mom, so you will need to be patient and encourage the piglet to use it. Sometimes in severe cases, when the pig won't nurse on the bottle, I put some milk in a bowl and, using a syringe, put it directly in their mouth while keeping their head level. This allows the piglet to realize that what you are feeding them is good and will potentially entice them to use the bottle.

The ultimate goal with bottle feeding is to get the piglet strong enough to go back into the barn with the rest of the litter and mom. I often switch the piglet from the bottle to drinking milk replacer out of a bowl to get to this point. I do this so that if they start to fall behind again, I can put a bowl of milk replacer in there where mom can't get it and that piglet has access to the milk replacer and mom. Additionally, using a bowl is much easier than feeding with a bottle.

Bottle feeding can occur at any point between birth and weaning, so be prepared for it at any given time. Being proactive and acting fast when a piglet starts to show that they need extra help can be the difference between life and death.

If I cannot get fresh goat milk or pig milk replacer, I use this.

Aside from keeping an eye on health and intervening, when necessary, there is another step to making sure that your piglets become the best that they can be, and that is to socialize them.

Tip 30: Socialize your litter

When these piglets leave your farm, they will start training to be show pigs. This will be easier for them to accomplish if they are socialized and unafraid of humans. I recommend spending lots of time in the barn with the whole litter, rubbing and petting them, and getting them used to your presence. I start this by sitting by them while they eat or while they sleep. This way, they are distracted, and while I pet them, they are undisturbed. Just by sitting with them, you are getting them used to being around people, which will desensitize them before they go off to become show pigs down the line. Also, the gentler the piglet is when it leaves the farm, the more reputable of a breeder you are, meaning your pigs will do better, and buyers will recommend you to others.

Now that your sow has had her litter, she gets a diet change that is well deserved, which leads me to maintenance and sow care.

Tip 31: Maintenance and sow care

When your sow has a litter, she starts to lactate and nurse her piglets, which takes a lot of energy and calories out of her. While she is lactating, she should be on a lactating grain, as well as on full feed. If she eats 15 pounds per day, let her eat 15 pounds per day. The more she can eat, the more milk she will produce for her litter, and the less likely she is to lose pounds when you wean the litter from her. You will need to transition her from the gestation grain she was eating before farrowing to the lactation grain; she will need to be eating while nursing her litter.

Additionally, your sow needs to stay hydrated. At the same time, she is lactating, so for the first day, sometimes longer, I will add a bottle of clear Pedialyte to her waterer to ensure that she has electrolytes and is hydrated for producing milk. I always use the clear one because it is least likely to give your sow an allergic reaction to the flavors or food dyes. They love the taste of it, so drinking it should not be an issue for her. You could even go as far as to give her the bottle of Pedialyte directly rather than in her waterer to make sure that she gets what she needs.

Another thing that is important to recognize is that your sow is in a farrowing crate, and she cannot pick an area to go to the bathroom. Therefore, her barn should be spot cleaned every day to ensure her cleanliness. Additionally, with her being in a crate, she will need some breaks from the litter and walks. These often only last about 10 minutes before she wants back in with her litter to take care of them, but it would be in her best interest to let her out for about 10 minutes per day. It allows her to get a walking break, and it will enable you to do whatever it is that you need to do while she is out. This is usually when I clean out her barn, give piglets shots when they need them, or do any repairs the barn may need in terms of removing the crate, putting up walls, fixing waters, etc. Your sow will be thankful, and it will also make things easier for you to do.

Speaking of giving piglets shots, this leads me to the next tip, which has to do with what shots the piglets need in the first week of their life.

Tip 32: Day two requirements

Day two is a big day for a litter of piglets. On this day, they need to receive one vaccine and need their tails docked as well. The dosage for the vaccine is on the bottle, so follow as directed. Iron is good for the piglets because it prevents them from becoming anemic. When the piglets have no access to the soil or dirt, anemia can set in within 7-10 days after birth, so iron is essential to prevent them from developing anemia. This injection should be given intramuscularly (in the muscle) behind the ear in the neck. This is the easiest place to give them, especially if you are doing it on your own.

66

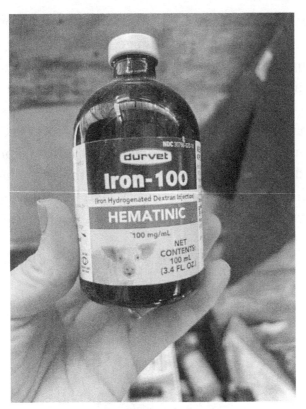

Bottle of Iron injection

he other thing that I mentioned that needs to happen on day two s the docking of their tails. This is especially important in show igs because it gives them more eye appeal. An undocked pig tail is xtremely long and is undesirable in appearance for show rings. dditionally, it is helpful to dock the tails because it makes it harder or the pigs to fight by biting and grabbing onto the tail. When I ock tails, I always do this on day two since it will be easier and less raumatic for them. I dock the tail after giving the pig each of the hots because when I set them down, they are pulling away from 1e, and as I dock the tail, it puts the appropriate amount of ressure to make it easier to dock. I use the tooth nippers that I sed at farrowing because they are sharp and easy to cut with. To 1easure, I often use the tip of my index finger; I measure from the tip of the tail at my top joint to the tip of my finger. Typically, a piglet's tail is about 2 inches at this age, but some are shorter, and some are longer, so cut accordingly. I usually leave about an inch or so behind when I dock tails. I cut the tail off, and then I will take iodine and spray it onto the tail to prevent infection. It's an easy, essentially pain-free procedure that the piglets forget about a few minutes after it happens. Some farmers wait until the piglet is a week old to do this, and some of them dock the entire tail. Yet with my experience, it is better to do it early, and it is more eye appealing to have a small tail rather than no tail at all.

Approximately how short the tails should be cut when docking.

The next big thing that piglets go through in week one is castration, or the removal of testicles to prevent breeding.

Tip 33: Remove those testicles

When the litter is about seven days old, this is when I castrate all the little boys. This is a difficult thing to do on your own, so be sure to have someone who can help you do this.

Castration is extremely important because if it is not done, pigs would have their testicles up until they get butchered. When the testicles are removed, male pigs become barrows, but while they have them, they are called boars. Boars are undesirable in the show ring unless it is a goal to raise them for breeding because pigs go to the butcher after the show. When a pig still has its testicles, its body is full of testosterone. This hormone makes the meat taste extremely gamey and just gross in general. Therefore, we castrate, and old boars are often only used for sausage rather than prime cuts of meat because they do not taste good.

There are many ways to go through removing the testicles, but I have found that it is easiest to have one person cut and one person to hold. The person who is cutting needs to have a scalpel or a sharp box knife, a shop towel, and iodine. The person holding just needs to find a comfortable place to sit. First, the person holding should hold the piglet upside-down, facing outwards. Then, holding onto the back legs and front legs simultaneously, holding the piglet together to keep them still while also puckering the testicles out where they can be seen. At this age, the testicles should have dropped and be easily visible. This is why I do this procedure at this age rather than younger.

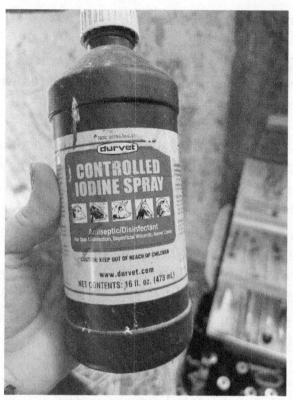

Iodine spray bottle.

The person who is cutting will push the testicles into place where they will be easiest to access and cut one slit where each one is (total of two cuts). Make the cuts small but just big enough to squeeze the testicle out. Once the cut is made, put pressure underneath the testicle to squeeze it out of the incision. Once it is out, it will truly pop out, grab the testicle and pull until taught, then cut as far away from the testicle as possible (getting as much tube as you can) and place it on the shop towel. Repeat this process for the other side, and then once both testicles are removed, spray the incisions with iodine.

The faster you move while doing this, the easier it will be on the piglet, so move quickly to get it done fast. Another tip would be to remove the sow from the barn and give her a walk at this time. If she is in the barn while this is happening, the piglets screaming will upset her, and she will be jumping up and down. Also, although the piglets should be aware of her legs at this point, she will be moving more frantically to get to her piglet and won't be paying attention to the rest of her litter, making it easier to step or lay on one of them.

One week old is a big day for the litter; not only do all the boys get castrated, but this is also the day they can start eating solid food and drinking water.

Tip 34: Start that piglet diet

At one week old, their stomachs are strong enough to start eating their own food and drinking water on their own. Piglets need to be on a high protein grain to feed their growing bodies, so it is essential that you get a nursery or starter feed. If you buy grain from the feed store, anything that says "starter-grower" should be good for them. These grains will likely have the higher protein content that the litter needs. If you are unsure which one to grab, ask the animal health associate on the clock at the time to get guidance with which brand to purchase. If I am buying from the feed store, my two favorite brands are "Country Companion" and "Nutrina" however, I have used "Purina," and they have what you need as well. However, I get my grain from a feed mill, so the grain I purchase is specially formulated for young litters, called "nursery" grain. This is fed to piglets until they are about 50 pounds and can be switched to a grower feed.

This is also the time that the farrowing crate can be pulled out of the barn, so with the grain, it is important to have bumper walls built to keep mom away from the nursery grain. I will also put a small feed pan of water behind the bumper wall to ensure the piglets have access to their own water source. These bumper walls need to be far enough from the wall to keep mom from accessing and breaking the heat lamp, eating the grain, or drinking the water, and give the litter plenty of space to sleep back there if they wish, so make sure you have a few feet of space for all of these things. I generally use two 2x4s to build my walls, with a short one on either side and in the middle to support. I leave enough room for the babies to get underneath the boards (6in or so) but still keep mom out. Then I run another one above that about the same spacing to keep mom from going over the top of the boards.

Week number one is a big one for the litter, potentially the biggest because of all the things that they need in those first seven days. From shots to tail docking, castrating, to new foods, there is a lot to do that first week, but each step is crucial and necessary to have a successful litter of show pigs.

Week Two for Your Litter

While not as exciting as week one, week two still has a few steps in it that affect you as a breeder and the health of the litter.

Tip 35: Keep those worms from invading

At about two weeks old, I do my first round of deworming for the piglets. As I have stated before, I use Noromectin. It is an injectable wormer that can be used in cattle, swine, and other livestock. I like to use this with my litters and my sows because it is the easiest to give, ensuring that they receive the correct dosage. I always deworm at this age, even if the piglets are not showing signs of having worms, to help prevent them from acquiring them. However, you should be aware of the signs of worms in piglets in case you have not wormed but need to do so.

The two big signs I notice with my piglets are pot bellies and diarrhea. When a pig needs to be wormed, its belly will become distended and look larger, almost like a potbelly. Additionally, they will have very soft stools or diarrhea. At this point, it is clear that the pig needs to be wormed. Sometimes, one can even see the worms in the pig's diarrhea, which is a clear sign that a dose of wormer needs to be given.

Bottle of Noromectin livestock dewormer.

Worming is not the only medicine pigs need at about two weeks old. There are other shots that they need, which leads me to tip number 6.

Tip 36: Keep the piglets healthy for longer

There are a lot of diseases that piglets are especially susceptible to at a young age, and beyond that, we vaccinate to ensure they never get those illnesses. One of which needs to be given at 7-10 days old. I typically wait till they are ten days old; since day 7 is such a big one for the litter, I give them a couple of days to relax and recoup. At ten days old, the whole litter needs a dose of "Rhinishield." This is a vaccine used in healthy pigs to help prevent the atrophic rhinitis caused by Bordetella bronchiseptica. It is an illness that affects the lungs of pigs and should be vaccinated against when they are at a young age. They need a 1ml dose at 7-10 days old, and then another dose of 2ml 2 weeks later (at about three weeks old). Like most other vaccines, this should be given intramuscularly, and I typically give it behind the ear in the neck.

Another vaccination that piglets need at this point is Vitamin B. This should be given at 7-10 days old as well. I inject this for my piglets because the B vitamins help to convert food into energy and to grow. When piglets are so young, they are fighting to stay alive by eating as much as possible. To assist them with this, it is important to ensure they have the vitamins that will help them succeed in converting their food into energy.

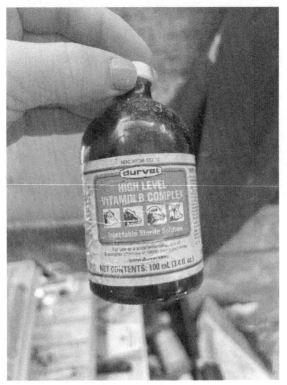
Bottle of Vitamin B injection.

Aside from keeping your piglets healthy, this is a big week for them because this is the age that I recommend allowing buyers to pick which hog they want from the litter.

Tip 37: Pick of the litter

Aside from keeping your piglets healthy, this is a big week for them because this is the age that I recommend allowing buyers to pick which hog they want from the litter.

Wet chalk stick. Useful for marking piglets that have been picked and are thus, not available.

One thing to be sure of while folks are picking their pigs, they do not go into the pen unless their shoes and all exposed clothing are sanitized. Piglets are extremely susceptible to a multitude of diseases and illnesses, and even if it is not their intention, anyone who is not from the farm could make your pigs sick. This goes for anyone who is visiting, too, even with the sows. I never let anyone into my barns unless they disinfect their shoes and keep their distance from the pigs.

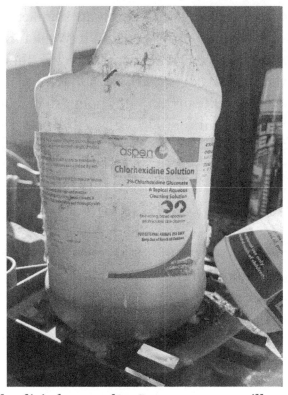

This is the disinfectant that I use to prevent illnesses from spreading.

I made a mistake one year of letting kids go into my pens when they were picking their pigs. This was fine until I had pigs dropping like flies with strep less than a week later. It took a full week to determine what they had because they each had different symptoms such as blindness, leg paralysis, coughing, fatigue, vomiting, and some were lethargic. We finally stopped the spread and saved most of my litter, but some of the pigs who got sick had long-lasting effects with swelling in their joints that impaired their walking abilities. Since then, I have been very strict with my cleanliness protocol because you never know what someone may have on their clothes and not know it.

As I stated before, week two for piglets is anticlimactic. They have a few shots, get picked out, but that's about it. Week three is similar to week two because not much happens; however, they receive some crucial vaccinations in week three, and they go through the biggest change in their life up until this point, so it is important to discuss this week in detail.

Week Three for Your Litter

Week three is a big one for your litter because they go through their first big change; weaning from mom. Additionally, they need some vaccinations at this age, so it is crucial to keep track of their age to ensure they get their vaccinations at the correct time.

Tip 38: More vaccinations are key

When the piglets turn three weeks old, they are at the age when they need most of the big vaccinations that protect them from a few different illnesses. Upon turning three weeks old, the three big ones that I give are mycoplasma vax, circoflex vax, and the porcine reproductive and respiratory syndrome vaccine. There is a package that is available on valley vet supply that includes all of these in one. These vaccines should be given at three weeks old and then given again two weeks later. These are also vaccines that should be given semi-annually to breeding swine. Respiratory diseases are extremely common in pigs and can be very deadly, so I always make sure to vaccinate against them to prevent future illnesses.

After the pigs are vaccinated with all that there is to give, it is time to wean them.

Tip 39: Be sure they are secure when weaning

Weaning can be stressful for your litter and your sow at the same time. It is a lot for them to handle, so it is crucial that you do so in the least stressful way possible. It is best if you have a place where you can move your sow to, rather than moving the piglets. This is because then they are only going through one change, compared to going through two; removal from mom and a new environment. As stated before, piglets can lose weight and look a little scraggly after weaning, and this is due to stress. It is possible to avoid this if the stress on the litter is limited.

Additionally, no matter what pen mom gets put into and where the litter is, it is important to create a secure environment that she cannot get out of. Some sows miss their litter and try to escape to get to them. So, it is important to have a pen where not only is she secure, but also the litter is secure in case she gets out and tries to get back to them.

After weaning, piglets can drop in health if they are not watched closely. In addition, since they are not receiving milk anymore, they may take a hit from these calories they are not used to missing. Therefore, it is crucial that they are observed closely.

While week three doesn't have a lot that happens out of the ordinary, the vaccinations they receive are still necessary, and weaning is a huge part of their transition from piglets to show pigs, but now, it is time to move on to week four.

Week Four for Your Litter

In the fourth week of their life, your piglets go through one of the biggest transitions of their life, need to be wormed again, and your sow should get ready for being bred again.

Tip 40: Keep a close eye

Not only can piglets drop weight after weaning, but they can stop eating. This week is a holding week between weaning and moving the piglets to their new homes. This week allows you, as the breeder, to ensure they are eating grain and drinking water as they should before they leave. If you notice that your piglets are not doing this, holding them for a week or two longer than anticipated may be necessary. Keep your buyers aware of their progress as they go through this transition. Also, you will need to keep an eye on your sow as well. She should be transitioned over to regular sow grain and back onto a regular ration (three pounds per day). You should keep a close eye on her to ensure that she doesn't start to drop excessive amounts of weight during this time. The stress and the diet change could cause excess weight to be lost, so keep an eye on her and increase feed ration temporarily if she starts to do this.

About two weeks ago, you wormed your litter. Well, before they go to their new home, they should be wormed again just in case. So, make sure to do this before they go to the buyer. If you do not do this, be sure to inform the buyer of the last time that the pigs were wormed so that they can worm according to a schedule of their own This leads me to the next tip, making a list of vaccines given.

Tip 41: Create a list of vaccines given

Whenever I have a litter of pigs, I always make a spreadsheet with the list of vaccines each pig got and what day. These are typically just the general ones such as iron, vitamin B, Rhinishield, etc. But additionally, I include the injections of antibiotics pigs get as well. So, for example, if a piglet had an issue and needed LA 200, I would put that on their sheet. This ensures the buyer is aware of what their hog was given and on what day.

Additionally, it would be helpful to include on the sheet when the pig is due for another dose of each one if it is a repeating vaccination. This would be especially beneficial for worming if you are not going to give it again before they leave. This way, the buyer is aware of the worming schedule.

Additionally, on this sheet, I make sure to include the ear notch number, the birthdate, the color, and any other information that may be beneficial, such as the sire or grandsire (dad or granddad on the sow side). Showmen love to know as much as they can about the hogs that they are buying so that they can talk about them while at the show, so this is beneficial for their sake.

Another sheet that would be beneficial to send with the vaccine record would be the "quality assurance" form if your area requires one for fair. This is simply a piece of paper that shows the transaction between the producer and the buyer of the hog and is needed for the hog to enter the fair. Providing this sheet upfront prevents any confusion down the line of trying to figure out how to get the form to the buyer from you with your information on it. It is just easier to provide it with the rest of their paperwork when they get the hog.

The next big thing that happens at the end of week four is your buyer gets to come to get their future show partner! As long as everything looks good, this will be when the buyer can come to pick up their hog and take them home to start training.

Tip 42: Sell your show pigs

This is the biggest thing that happens in week four. When your litter reaches four weeks old, they are old enough to go to their new homes to become show pigs. To make for an easy transition, when your buyer comes to pick up their pig, make sure you have all the papers that are listed above and provide your contact information. Additionally, it would be in the pig's best interest to provide a gallon bag of feed to help them transition if they won't be on the same grain they are currently used to. If they get switched on grain too abruptly, it could cause their stomach to get upset, and they could develop diarrhea. Also, you should inform the buyer of any products you recommend or grain brands you recommend as well. As the producer, you are going to be a great resource for the buyer if they are unsure what to look for, so provide some tips while they are there to give them confidence that they can count on you. Therefore, the contact information between you and the buyer should stay current in case they need training tips or have inquiries down the road.

When the buyer picks up the pig, I normally have a scale on-site so that I can weigh each pig as it leaves the farm. This gives the buyer an idea of how much they are growing and when they should transition to the grower feed (they transition to the grower at 50 pounds). Additionally, this will tell you how much the pigs have been growing over the last few weeks, giving you a better grasp on how they were doing, considering the grain change and different stresses they went through.

Now that your litter is gone, aside from any that you have kept for yourself, it is time to start thinking about training your pigs and also getting ready for the next litter. After weaning, your sow will come back into heat 3-10 days later, so you will need to start thinking about when to breed your sow next.

Tip 43: Rebreed your sow

During week four, after you have weaned the litter from mom, your sow should come back into heat 3-10 days after the weaning day. I generally don't like to breed back immediately after weaning because I like to give my sow at least one heat cycle to recoup and gain back her strength from breeding. Yet sometimes, we do not have that luxury. It is important to identify when you should breed again for the next set of shows. When I have litters in the fall, I have to rebreed right away to ensure I have litters at the right time (around Valentine's Day), but when I have litters born in the spring, I don't have to rebreed for a few months. Keep track of your sow's cycle and determine when you should rebreed, and if you need to breed right away, be ready to order semen once she comes into heat during this week to get her caught the first time. Every sow is different, so you will have to take note and be aware of how your sow is behaving after you wean your litter.

Chapter Review:

- Day one, keep track of the health of your piglets and your sow.
- Know where to locate milk replacer if needed, always pig milk replacer or goat milk/replacer. These are the only options if a piglet needs extra help.
- Dock tails: it is much more eye appealing and prevents fighting down the road.

- Keep up on all the vaccinations and worming that they need from day one all the way to week four.
- Keep track of their vaccinations and deworming on a spreadsheet to give the buyer when they collect the pig.
- Advertise and create a commitment list of buyers for your pigs.
- Allow buyers to pick out their pigs at two weeks old and have them provide you with a 50% down payment for their pig to secure their spot on your list.
- Have a cleanliness protocol for anyone visiting the farm. This protects your pigs from any outside diseases that someone may be carrying unknowingly.
- Keep piglets and mom very secure after weaning to prevent mom from getting to your litter after they are weaned.
- Know when to add food for the piglets to eat and know what feed ration mom should be on while lactating and right after weaning.

Chapter 4: Next Steps of Raising Show Hogs

All but your show pigs from the litter have left the farm; you only have a few left. So now, what do you do? It can be intimidating moving forward, trying to determine how to raise and train these hogs to be prime and quality show hogs. This chapter will guide you through the steps of what to do immediately after you sell your litter and are left with just your show pigs behind.

Type of Pen

Similar to raising your sows, it is crucial to have your pig in the correct type of stall to ensure they stay healthy, safe, and clean up until the show. In this section, I will talk about how to set up the perfect show pigpen, the type of bedding, how often to clean, and how to keep your pigs clean.

Tip 44: Smallest is best

Unlike your sow, show pigs do not need a lot of room to be comfortable. Their barns can be a lot smaller than your sow's because they are not here as long, and they do not get as big. Additionally, they should get used to the smaller areas because while at the shows, the pens are even smaller, sometimes only 4'x4' in area. All of my barns are the same size in case I have to move my sow to a different barn sporadically, and they need to be an adequate size, but if you are building a pen strictly for your show pigs, it doesn't need to be as big as the barns for your sows are. You should also make sure to keep your pigs separated. If you have more than one show pig, have them in separate barns to keep track of their individual progress. I like to keep them next to each other to ensure that they stay familiar because when they go to the fair, they will have to share a stall; however, until then, it is best to keep them separate for feeding reasons. So, make sure that you not only have barns that are adequate size, but you also have enough for the number of show pigs you have.

Two show pigs housed in an adequately sized pen.

Now that you have the dimensions, you should consider the material. Since the barns are temporary for my show pigs, I generally use wood because they are not there for very long and do not need the structure to be as stable. I will typically put my show pigs in a barn that is older than my other ones because show pigs are generally less destructive than your sows, and they are smaller, so they do not need the structure to be as sturdy. However, I always make sure they are in an area that is hardwood. This leads me to tip number 45.

Tip 45: Hardwood is Best

Hardwood or hard floors are best for your show pigs for multiple reasons. One reason is that they are the easiest to clean. If you have your show pigs outside in the dirt, it is hard to keep the area clean, which is extremely important. Additionally, having hard floors helps keep your pigs' leg structure correct, and concrete, specifically, will help to keep your pigs' toes filed down and short so that they do not grow too long. It is sturdy, clean, and best for the pig's structure, so I always use hard floors in all of my barns. Wood is the easiest for me to build because it is the most accessible resource, but if concrete is a possibility for you, the barns will be longer-lasting, and your pigs will thank you.

One of the reasons I mentioned that I use hardwood floors instead of soft floors is cleanliness. Cleanliness is essential, so this leads me to the next tip.

Tip 46: Cleanest is best

Pigs are commonly known for being unclean animals; on the contrary, they are extremely clean. They will pick an area to go to the bathroom far away from where they lay down since they do not want to lay in their own filth. Their pens need to be cleaned out at least once a week to help them stay clean. In my show pig pens, I typically do what I call a spot clean every day, where I go through with my pitchfork and pick up any mess they made that day. This helps me stay on top of everything during the week and keeps them from getting too messy. These pigs need to stay clean for the show, so it is best to keep them clean the whole time to ensure they do not acquire stains before going to the show.

Additionally, there is a certain type of bedding that is best for keeping the pigs clean without causing their hair to have stains. Unlike in the farrowing barn, where it is best to use straw for warmth, I always use pine shavings in my show pig pens. In my personal experience, I have found that shavings do not absorb as much moisture, and it prevents the pigs from getting muck and water stains in their hair. Additionally, I always use pine shavings because the alternative of cedar causes allergic reactions on their skin. When using cedar, pigs often get small red bumps all over their sides and their bellies wherever they have contacted the shavings, so for this reason, I always use pine over cedar.

Another factor that ties into having a clean pig is having a place where the pig can be washed daily. This is harder in the winter due to the colder temperatures, but a wash rack is crucial for the cleanliness and to keep them cool in the summer.

Tip 47: Build a wash rack

Wash racks are built to be an area where you can wash your pig daily. This is important because a big part of being in the show ring is having an extremely clean pig. This is a different situation for the pigs, so getting them used to being washed will be beneficial to them, and it is easier to have a clean pig at fair if they are clean every day leading up to fair. My wash racks are typically hard floors, but they do not need to have a roof over the top. These are best built when they are small (4'x4') and have paneled sides with a small gate. It is even better if you can create a floor with holes in it to have water drain through. The wash rack should be close to a faucet where you can hook up a hose, and it should be easily accessible. Washing will not come until your pig is old enough to start training, but it is important to have one ready, for whenever it is time to start training that show pig.

With all this talk about having the correct pen and an area where your pig can stay clean, it is time to start talking about the diet your pig should be on, how to build their trust, and all the things that come right after you have sold your litter and are left with your own show pigs.

A Show Pig Diet

Show pigs should be kept on a reasonable diet; however, it does not need to be as strict as the diet that your sow is kept on. Additionally, food is a big tool used to build trust with your show pig. In fact, it is the first tool that I use to build trust, for it is the most effective tactic.

Tip 48: Feeding your pig appropriately

Pigs gain weight with the ratio of one pound of weight gained per three pounds of grain eaten. This is approximate, of course, because some pigs could be on full feed and never gain anything, but it is the general rule of thumb that is used across the board with all pigs. Since show pigs are trying to get to a specific weight in a short amount of time, I generally have my pigs on a diet that is just below full feed. To determine how much your pigs should be eating to gain the right about of weight, you should determine what the lowest weight your pig has to be in order to enter the show and what the maximum weight is that they can be. For example, all the fairs around me have a weight range of 235 pounds to 290 pounds. This means that if the pig is less than 235 pounds, it cannot enter the fair, and if it is over 290, it cannot enter the fair. Next, you should determine how long your pig has to get to the weight they are required to be at. Generally, pigs are 6-8 months old at the fair, so this should be an indicator of how long you have to get your pig to the appropriate weight.

To make sure that my pigs are gaining as much weight as possible, I have them just below what is called "free feeding." "Free feeding" is when you have grain in front of your pig at all times, never letting them be empty. Now, this may seem like the best tactic; however, if a pig has grain 24/7, they never get hungry, and they are not inclined to eat food. If you only give them exactly what they need to be full, then they still get a little hungry and will eat more. Also, this ensures that you will be feeding your pig at least once a day (hopefully twice), which will make your pig associate you with receiving food. This will help build trust with your pig, which leads me to tip number 49.

Tip 49: Build trust with your show pig

In order to have a strong bond and relationship with your show pig, it needs to be a relationship built on trust. The easiest way to do this is to spend time with your pig and get them to associate you with food. Pigs are very food-driven animals, so the use of food is the best way to get them to trust you. This is one of the reasons that I like to make sure that I am feeding my pigs twice a day. During feeding time, especially when they are young, I will pour the feed into the pan and have the pigs come to me to eat their grain. I will also have treats in my pocket to give them if they come close. Pigs love candy of all kinds, so I will use M&Ms, licorice, or even marshmallows as treats for my pigs when I am building trust. By doing this every day, you are getting the pigs more and more used to your presence, which will help them to be a better partner in the show ring. This is easier to do when you have raised the pigs from farrowing, but if you buy a show pig from another producer, this can be more difficult, which is why it is more crucial.

As you are getting your pig(s) used to you bringing them food, you can start to pet and rub them to get them used to your touch as well. You will need to rub your pig everywhere to keep them clean and show them in the ring, so getting them used to your touch is also important.

With your pig building trust with you and needing to be at a specific weight for fair, some pigs grow at different rates, so it is important to know how to adjust or adapt their feeding to meet their needs adequately.

Tip 50: Know how to adjust feed appropriately

Some pigs grow extremely slow, and others take off like a rocket when put on grain. For each of these types of pigs, there are tips and tricks to gain weight at the appropriate rate for them.

If your pig is gaining weight too fast, the biggest thing is to give them substance without giving them the calories. These pigs can be brought back on grain by including a ration of beet pulp in their diet. Beet pulp is a type of feed that is very low in calories but full of substance, so the pig still feels like it is eating a lot of food. I typically mix beet pulp with three pounds of grain per day for these pigs to give them food and fill up their stomachs, keeping them from having a huge appetite. This keeps the pigs from getting too hungry, but they still get the nutrients they need from the grain in the mixture.

If your pig has too much fat on them, becoming flabby rather than muscular and even-toned with the appropriate amount of fat to muscle ratio, then one way to slim off some fat is to feed them oats. I usually provide this with a 1:1 ratio. Oats do wonders for slimming off the fat that is unwanted with pigs. They tend to pick around them because they prefer to eat food with more sustenance, but if you leave it long enough, they will eat enough to take off any unwanted fat.

If you have a pig that isn't gaining enough weight, one of the things that you can do is to add milk, soda, and cake mix into the feed. Feed as much grain as the pig can eat, and add in a box of cake mix, ¼ liter of soda, and about half a gallon of milk. The milk weighs down the stomach better than water, so it can help pack on the pounds. Additionally, the fat in the milk, along with the proteins, can also help build on the muscle and fat in the pig to help with weight gain. The other additives are strictly calorie enhancers and have to do with encouraging the pig to eat more food. This mixture has been used and proven to work on pigs that I had that were on the lighter weight side and were on the edge of not making weight. After using this mixture on my light pigs, they weighed in on at least 250 pounds each, when I was worried about them making weight at 235 pounds. Another trick that I have used to help my pigs gain weight is to water down the feed. This helps keep them hydrated and makes the grain easier for them to digest and eat, encouraging them to eat, therefore, gain more weight.

A hog that needed the cake mixture to gain weight, waiting patiently for his treat.

Another thing that you can add to your feed for extra protein for your hog is raw fresh eggs. They can even eat the shells for the calcium if they are fresh from the farm. I typically use this trick in my pigs that are on the light end and could use the extra muscle mass. Typically, one to two eggs a day should do the trick.

For the reasons listed above, it is always best to keep your pigs separate to accommodate their specific dietary needs. Each pig is different, even from the same litter, and they may need to be on entirely different dietary schedules and recipes. I always separated my pigs once they reached 50 pounds and started on the grower feed so that I could keep track of their specific progress. Additionally, when you separate pigs, they are more likely to get what they need because they do not need to fight over food. When pigs are together, one of them is almost always the dominant one and, therefore, is the heavier one. Yet, if they are separated, they each have their own opportunity to get what they need to grow.

Chapter Review:

- Set up a show pig pen that is the appropriate size and easy to manage regarding cleanliness.
- Build a wash rack to wash your pig when they are dirty, to prevent stains from accumulating on their hair.
- Build your pig's trust by using food to entice them to build a relationship with you.
- Keep your pigs separate so that you can keep track of their eating progress and ensure each of them gets what they need.
- Know how to accommodate each of your pigs' specific needs regarding their weight gain. Know when to add more fat and protein or when to implement some calorie-free substance or oats.

Chapter 5: Training Your Quality Show Hog

The biggest part of raising a show pig is getting them ready to perform in the show ring. This means extensive training once they are old enough, up until the show actually starts. This is why the trust-building from the last chapter is so important. In this chapter, I will talk about the training basics, different types of tools that are useful, and the first steps to getting started.

Getting Started

In this section of the chapter, I will discuss how to get started with the training of your hog. The first and most important thing is to start slow and have patience.

Tip 51: Start slow and be patient

You have to remember that this is the first time your pig has done this, so they will be easily frustrated and willing to give up. I typically start small by using a simple, rubber-tipped whip. This type of whip is most effective, especially with training a new hog. To start, I always use light taps only in the pen where the pig resides. This gets the pig used to following the whip direction, and you get a feel for how the pig will react. This only works if there is enough room in the pen, so if there is not, then you will have to venture out.

When I start training for a new pig, I tend to let them get used to five minutes at a time first; only five minutes of walking to start. They have to get used to the training, but they also need to build their stamina. Your pig will get to a point where they could be walking for 15-20 minutes no problem, but you have to work up to that point. Always push them a little bit farther than their stamina wants to go. Then, when they start to fuss, go for one minute more. This shows them that they don't stop when they want to, that you are in control, and it also builds their stamina. However, you don't want to push them too hard right from the get-go.

Additionally, patience is key. Your pig is not going to understand what you want from them right away. It will take time to understand what their job is and why you want them to do what you are having them do. It will be confusing for them at first, so be patient and give them time to figure it out.

Now that you understand that they need to be started slow, and patience is key to a successful show relationship, we can get started on technique and how to train your pig.

Tip 52: Head and shoulders

When whip training a pig, there are three areas that you focus on for driving.

- Head
- Neck
- Shoulder/side

These three areas are the only areas where your whip should make contact with the pig. The neck and head contact is used to have your pig drive with their head to the sky. This is extremely desirable in the show ring. The higher your pig's nose is, the more eye-appealing they will be and the slower they will walk. When a pig walks with their nose to the sky, they elongate their neck, arching their structure, and it smooths out their gait, making them look more structurally correct.

The other area, the shoulder and side, is where your whip will make contact to keep your pig driving at a reasonable speed. If your pig is going too slow, it will appear that your pig is only leisurely walking and isn't listening to you. It also keeps them going at their pace if they know that you are encouraging them to drive forward.

These taps of contact are just that, taps. You should not be fully whipping or hitting your pig with the whip. The taps that are used to encourage the pig to keep moving should be light, not hard or aggressive. This is a partnership with your pig, not a dominance or control factor. You should be working with your pig rather than against it.

While you are driving, to go straight, you will alternate tapping each side of the pig's face to encourage them in that direction until they understand. To turn either way, you will tap that side of the face/neck to encourage them. For example, turning to the left, you will tap on the right side; going to the right, you will tap on the left side. Additionally, to encourage them to carry their nose to the sky, these taps around the face should be upward brushing taps. Learning to drive can also be accompanied by using two whips, one in each hand on either side of the pig's face. This will encourage them to carry their face higher, and the brushing movements gently coax them to get to that point.

If your pig is starting to go too fast, and having them drive their nose higher isn't working, you can do a quick tap on the top of the head down to the nose to slow them down. Do this sparingly so as not to encourage having a low head while driving, but this can be used to teach them the pace at which you wish them to walk.

Now that you understand how to get started with training your pig and the basics, there are a few different tools that you can use to train them when it comes to whips and head trainers.

Tip 53: Pick out the right tool

Each pig is different and has its own preferences. Some like the soft tassel, some like the hard rubber ends. Others may prefer the whips that have a dangle, or maybe your pig prefers one with a paddle on the end. Each one has its benefits and reasons for using it.

Soft Tassel: This whip is my favorite one to use in the show ring, especially on the first day. It is flashy and professional-looking. The first show is all about first impressions, so you want to look your best, even if it is only the market class. This whip is effective if you have a very sensitive pig that is receptive to even the slightest touch. However, if you have an unruly pig that needs more structure, this whip may not be enough for them to follow directions in the show ring, and you may need a different whip. I had a pig that found this whip more annoying than guiding, so I couldn't use it on her, but I had another that would only listen to this type of whip. It all boils down to your pig's preferences.

Soft tassel whip

Rubber-Tipped Whip: This whip is easily my favorite for training, showing and being just all-around productive no matter the circumstance. The rubber tip ensures that the whip adds a little more structure, so you don't have to tap as hard. All of my pigs have at least tolerated this one over others, so it is my go-to whip for all situations. However, this one is not as professional looking compared to the tasseled whips, so in order to attract the eye of the judge, you will need to be skilled with maneuvering your hog correctly.

Rubber tipped whip.

Whip with A Paddle: These are potentially my least favorite whips because they make a slapping sound when they contact the pig. These are also least favorable in the show ring; however, when you are training an unruly hog, they can be extremely effective. These whips are designed to provide more structure and discipline if needed, so these should only be used on the farm during training. Again, I would not recommend using this in the show ring unless it is the only whip your pig will respond to.

Dangle on the End: These are another one of my favorite whips to use on a pig that needs a little bit extra encouragement. The whip adds more leverage for guiding the pig with the moveable end. This is especially useful in the show ring or at the farm while training. Although it is not as flashy as the tasseled type, there is a way to fray the end to make it softer and have a tasseled look while still providing the structure and discipline the pig may need. Again, these are very effective whips and are my favorites to use at a high-intensity show.

With all these whips listed above, it can be difficult to decide which one is the best option for you and your pig. The best way to do this is to have all of these options on hand and try them out. Then, see which one you and your show pig-like best. It will take some trial and error, but eventually, you will narrow it down to the best whip for you to use with your pig.

Another tool that is available to use while training your pig is what is called the "head trainer." This tool is designed to help teach your pig to walk with their head to the sky rather than level or down to the ground. I have never personally used this tool because I have never needed to, but I have heard that it is very beneficial to train a pig to drive properly. It is essentially a bent piece of plastic tubing that you use similarly to a whip to encourage head drive. Again, this should only be used while training, not in the show ring, as it is not a show tool; it is a training tool. These are not as readily available at the local feed stores, so you will likely need to order this tool online if you would like to try it out.

All of these tools listed above are great resources, but they aren't effective without a proper reward system. This leads to tip number 54.

Tip 54: Use rewards

When training a new pig to drive and show, they need to be enticed to put in the work. When I am working with a new hog, just like when building trust, I keep some treats in my pocket. This is similar to the tactic used while teaching a dog to walk properly on a leash. Giving a treat when the desired behavior is seen will help to encourage that behavior more frequently. Pigs are extremely smart, even more so than dogs, so they will learn quickly if they are trained correctly. This means giving them a lot of incentive and encouragement with what they truly want; food or treats.

Now that you know how to start training your pig and the first steps to turning them into a show ring champion, there are some basic routines and strategies that you can do to ensure you have the best hog in the ring.

Strategies to Build the Best Hog in the Ring

When in the show ring, you don't want to blend in with the rest of the crowd; you want to stand out to rise to the top. You won't be able to do that if you are doing what everyone else is doing, you will have to come up with tactics to use in order to stand out in the ring and bring the judge's eyes to you.

Tip 55: Driving Backwards

When you are in the ring, you should never ever let your pig or you touch the judge unless they ask you to. This shows that you have spatial awareness and are aware of where the judge is in proximity to you. Additionally, you should be able to show the judge every angle of your pig, meaning you should be able to show a front view, profile, rear view, angled, and any other angles that your judge may want to see. For the rear view, you will need to be able to walk away from the judge with your pig walking toward you. This is so that you can maintain eye contact with the judge like you are supposed to while still showing the different angles of your hog. To do this, you will need to gain enough control of your pigs to ensure they continue to walk towards you, even if you are standing in front of them. They will also need to trust you enough to be willing to walk

owards you like that. Again, this is something that should be
ntroduced after your pig has the basics of following your directions.

Tip 56: Be able to turn on a dime

n the show ring, you may not have control over where other people
will drive their hogs or if the judge will move at the last second and
get in front of you. Because of this, you will need to be able to turn
on a dime to avoid a potential obstacle. To practice this, I will set up
obstacles around my walking area, drive my pig towards it and then
turn at the last second or have them drive loops around the
obstacles. Of course, the faster you can do this with your pig, the
better off you will be in the show ring.

Another thing to keep in mind is the area you are driving your hog
in. It is easier on their feet to walk them in a grassy area. However,
walking up and down hills can help build the strong muscle tones
desired in a high-quality show hog. Yet the biggest influence on a
how hog's respect and trust is having an open area to drive your
hog. Some showmen will build a show ring at their farm to drive
their hogs in, but if your pig doesn't learn to listen to you without
fences or walls to keep them in, then the likelihood of them
respecting you when outside the fences is slim. The more they
practice without fences, the more they will respect you in the show
ring when stakes are high and the intensity is higher.

Chapter Review:

- Each pig is different, so understand that they may have a
  preferred whip for training and showing.
- Understand the different types of whips and their pros and
  cons to determine which is the best fit for you and your pig.

- Understand that going slow and patience is the key to starting a successful show career. Your pig is new to this, so be patient with them as they learn what you expect them to do.
- After they start to develop show skills, start to implement strategies that will help you stand out in the show ring with your showing.

Chapter 6: Show Quality Products to Use

In this chapter, we will be reviewing all of the products that I recommend for your show pig and your sows. These products are going to be related to the supplements, shampoos, and other skin care, as well as how you can go natural for both areas, if you wish. This will be your referencing guide for all the brands and products that I recommend as a previous showman and current show pig producer.

Shampoos and Other Skin Care

In this section, I will cover everything you need to take care of your pig's skin and hair. This includes the types of shampoo, conditioners, sprays, and other tips for having show ready hair. While in the show ring, your pig's cleanliness will stand out, but it never hurts to add a little shine to ensure all eyes are on your hog.

Tip 57: The best products to keep your pig clean

When driving your hog in the show ring, you want to stand out with their cleanliness. This means no stains or anything of the sort to give your judge negative things to say about your pig. There are a couple of products regarding shampoos that I recommend using on your pig.

The first product for shampoo for your pig that I recommend is the gallon-sized bottle of "Aloe Advantage Concentrated Shampoo." This shampoo is best paired with a sprayer that you attach to the hose with a compartment to put shampoo or soap. This is the easiest way to wash a pig that I have found, and it helps to make your soap last longer. This type of shampoo for all types of livestock is very beneficial to their hair and skin because it is made with aloe vera, a natural skin aid, and a moisturizer. I have used many products regarding shampoos, and this one has been my favorite to use.

The "Aloe advantage" concentrated shampoo that I use.

If you would prefer not to use a sprayer like the one that is listed, you may use a different brand of shampoo, and if that is the case, I recommend anything "Weaver." "Weaver" is my go-to brand for anything regarding livestock, so any of their shampoos are going to be the best formula for your pig's hair and skin to keep them fresh and clean.

As discussed before, there are different colors of pigs. Some types of pigs are easier to clean than others. If you have a pig that is calico or has any type of light coloring, they will be the hardest to keep clean because they will stain easier than your pigs with black or red on them. For these hogs, I recommend using a whitening shampoo.

Tip 58: Get yourself some purple shampoo

White or light-colored pigs are going to absorb color the fastest and in the most annoying way possible; through stains. Therefore, these pigs need extra care in keeping them clean and ready for the show ring. I use a purple or whitening shampoo for these pigs to keep their hair and skin white and bright.

There are two different brands that I recommend for whitening shampoo. The first is the "Weaver" brand called 'Shimmer Shampoo.' This shampoo is purple and will brighten all light colors in livestock, not just white. So if you have a gray hog or calico, this will be for you. It will brighten their hair and remove the stains faster than other brands, and your pig will be show-ready in no time.

A whitening shampoo from 'Weaver' that is very useful.

Another brand of whitening shampoo that I recommend for light-colored hogs is "Quiksilver." This shampoo is extremely effective in removing all kinds of stains from white hogs. However, I have never personally used this on a light-colored hog that wasn't just white, so that would be something to try. Additionally, this shampoo is more expensive than the "Weaver" brand, so the "Shimmer Shampoo" will be a bigger bang for your buck, but the "Quiksilver" is an option if the "Weaver" one isn't available to you or you wish to try a different route.

Aside from just washing your pig, there are other skincare needs that need to be met to ensure your pig is show ready, which leads me to the next tip.

Tip 59: Get an effective spray-on conditioner

Although shampoos are extremely important, even more so is how you take care of your pig's skin after they have gotten a bath. This is where spray-on shines and conditioner come into play. These can be used either after a bath or even right before the show starts to give your pig that extra shine to put an edge on the competition.

Another "Weaver" product. Works amazingly on black hogs.

The first skin conditioner I will recommend is the "Weaver Pink Stuff." This conditioner truly takes great care of your pig's skin and gives them the shine they need to stand out. It can be used on all colors of hogs and even smells good. This is my go-to conditioner for all of my hogs; I even use it on my sows when they start to get flakey skin. I often pair this conditioner with the "Weaver Pro Polish," which can be used on its own if you prefer. I do this by mixing the two sprays into a sprayer using a ratio of 1:1. This mixture adds a glossy shine to the hog's coat while moisturizing the hair and taking care of the skin as well. This is not only one of my favorite products to use, but a little goes a long way, so it lasts quite a while as well.

The "Pink Stuff" by weaver.

Another type of spray-on conditioner that I use is called "Show Sheen." This spray-on is best used on hogs with colors like black, blue, or red, but it can be used on other pigs if desired as well. When using this spray, it is best to spray it on, and then using a brush, brush the spray into the hair and skin. The conditioner gives the hog a wet shiny look that is subtle enough that the pig doesn't look sopping, but they have a finished, well-groomed look. Again, I say it is best used on hogs with color because, with white pigs, it doesn't make much of a difference in their appearance; it simply moisturizes the skin and hair. This product is great to use while preparing for the show and during the show, but if you want it to visibly make your hog shinier, using it on white pigs won't be as effective.

Show sheen spray.

While having a clean pig that is visibly ready for the show ring in appearance is important, your hog also needs to be ready by being finished properly with an appealing muscular build. There are supplements to get them to this point that can be crucial to the success of your hog in the show ring.

Supplements to Aid in Your Success

When in the show ring, the judge is going to look at the cleanliness of your hog, but they are going to first look at the build of your hog. A judge will look at their structural build, how muscular they are, and also the ratio of fat to muscle. There are supplements to make your hog's appearance more desired that can aid in your success.

Tip 60: Supplements for your overall needs

There are some supplements that are used to meet a multitude of needs, such as nutrition, fat supplement, muscle building, etc. These supplements are beneficial because if there is a hog that has more than one supplemental need, these supplements can be given to meet those needs simultaneously.

Before I get started, I want to mention that these are not the only pig supplements available; these are just ones that I would trust with my pig's health. Almost all of my products are purchased and received from "Valley Vet" online if I cannot find it at my feed store, so if you feel that one of these supplements isn't quite what you need, you can find other options on this website.

The first supplement for this tip I would like to mention is "Show Bloom Livestock Conditioner and Supplement." This feed ration is a great option because, for those who want to travel a more natural nutrition route, this supplement is an all-natural blend. This supplement is great for producing and maintaining a healthy coat, skin, and hooves. It also can aid in muscle development, feed intake, and utilization and helps the hogs meet their overall genetic potential. It is packed full of nutrients, vitamins, and amino acids that benefit the overall health of your hog. It is only an add-on that isn't a complete feed, with only 4 oz needed to be fed per day. This supplement will help you with the muscle and fat building of your hog, give them a vitamin balance for their overall health, and aid in the maintenance of their skin, coat, and hooves.

Another beneficial supplement for overall health is "Essential Smooth Silk." Similar to the last supplement, this is beneficial for a multitude of reasons. First, it is a liquid add-on for feed rations. Like the "Show Bloom Livestock Conditioner and Supplement," it is a fairly natural blend that can be given. Composing of natural vegetable fats, amino acids, fatty acids, and Vitamin E, this blend is great for improving the shine and softness of skin and coat on a pig and for muscle expression while maintaining weight gain. It also is very palatable because it is cherry flavored, so there shouldn't be a worry of pigs not eating it when it is added to feed rations.

While still beneficial for multiple reasons, the final supplement for this tip is for the benefit of breeding and market gilts. A show hog's intense high protein diet can make female hogs too bulky with a masculine appearance. For this reason, "Fresh & Feminine Fast Track for Show Pigs" can be fed to balance out the females and make them more feminine appearing. This supplement was generated to make gilts more feminine and eye appealing. Having a fresh front end and feminine appearance in the show ring can determine failure or success for a gilt. This supplement was specifically formulated to meet the needs of the market and breeding gilts by having a proper balance of amino acids, vitamins, and minerals. Female hogs look better when they have longer and leaner necks, which this supplement targets to ensure they are more appealing. Just like the other two supplements, it is not a complete ration and should be fed mixed with a normal feeding schedule of twice per day.

With these three supplements that target overall health in female and male hogs, there are also other supplements that can be added to aid in specific health needs. For example, some feed additives are specifically for fat or muscle building, strictly for nutrient needs, and others are for skin and coat care. This next tip will discuss the different types of supplements that should be used for fat conditioning.

Tip 61: Supplements for Fat Needs

When it comes to looking right in the show ring, hogs need to have the correct amount of fat cover to give them a finished look. Getting this point can be difficult to reach naturally because the show pig diet is so rich in protein that the fat can sometimes be late to show. So, to enhance this and get the pigs to their desired potential, sometimes fat supplements need to be implemented to give them the desired look.

The first supplement that can aid in the fat cover is a product called "Sumo." This is a fat supplement that, when given to pigs, makes them blossom. This product is a blend of aggressive fat sources and dairy products to give your hog the desired fat-conditioned look. With an incredible 70% fat ratio, your pigs will gain fat fast if given this. I usually only give this if a pig is behind and is at risk of not making weight if it's winter and the pig needs extra help with fat production, or when it is a couple of weeks before the show, so the hog needs the fat cover. It is important to note that this is not a complete feed ration, so your hog will need this to be mixed with their grain.

Another fat supplement that can be used to generate this condition in your hog is the supplement called "Chub it Up." This is another liquid supplement option that is less intense in comparison to the other fat supplement, "Sumo." This blend is not only good for adding a soft, fresh look, but it also helps add hair pop and shine in a hog. This supplement can be used to soften a hard topline or give them a fresher look.

With these two different types of supplements used for conditioning, there are also some hogs who struggle with building muscle, and they are too conditioned. When this is the case, muscle supplements can be added to strengthen their physique and make them stand out in the show ring.

Tip 62: Supplements for Muscle Needs

When it comes to standing out in the show ring, especially in the market class, the physical structure of a hog's muscle may be the most crucial factor to consider. Muscle translates to meat, and in the market class, the prime focus is how this hog would look as a meat-rearing carcass. Muscle supplements may be needed to help meet these needs. There is one specific supplement that I have used and seen to be extremely successful when it comes to this. This supplement is called "High Octane Fitter 35", and it is by *Purina*. This supplement has made a world of difference in the meat production for my hogs. It can be used for all livestock and is highly palatable. My hogs generally will pick out the supplement before eating their grain. If this supplement is properly paired with a high-protein show hog food, it will help get the hog to the physique that would be desired in the show ring.

While fat and muscles in a show hog are important, there are other types of supplements that can be used for more specific reasons related to health. These can be related to stress, nutrition, or even skincare. There were supplements that I mentioned that benefitted overall health with fat, muscles, and nutrition, but for hogs that are used for breeding, or they don't have fat or muscle needs, they need a supplement that is more specific.

Tip 63: Supplements for Nutrition Needs

There are two different supplements that I use daily in my show and breeding stock to keep their nutritional levels up and meet their health needs. The first one is "Dyne High-Calorie Liquid for

Livestock." This liquid supplement is just that, a calorie-dense blend that can help hogs if they need some calorie intake support or weight gain. The high-calorie factor is also beneficial for any hogs that are high stress or are in recovery. It provides stamina, extra energy, and weight gain. I use this with my sows when they are lactating, getting ready for labor, or are in heat and need to take a litter. Then in my show stock, I will use this in their daily feed ration to meet their calorie needs.

The other supplement related to nutritional needs that I use on a daily basis in all of my stock is "Equerry's Probiotics." Probiotics are extremely beneficial for all livestock because it helps with gut health and benefits them in huge ways. I mix this into the daily feed ration for each of my hogs because it is so beneficial to their health, helping them absorb nutrients from their feed and processing it to energy.

There are other supplements that are beneficial for other reasons, such as stress or skincare, which leads me to the next tip.

Tip 64: Supplement for Stress Needs

Going to a show can be highly stressful for hogs, especially if they have never been to a show before. There are so many other hogs; the pens are smaller, with all the people and commotion, it can be overstimulating and stressful for the hogs involved. For these reasons, whenever I travel to a show, I always make sure to have "Show Ease' in my tack box. This is a paste that can be given to a hog orally before going into the show ring or traveling a long distance. This paste helps to desensitize the hog and relax them prior to a stressful event. Yet, before actually using the paste for the stressful event, I would use this to make sure your hog doesn't have an unexpected reaction to the paste. This will inform you how your hog reacts, how long it takes to set in, and also how long it lasts. This will be important to know before the show because you will need to know how much to give them and whether it will be a beneficial item to use.

Show Ease stress relieving gel.

When it comes to skincare, there are other ways to ensure your animal has show quality skin and coat prior to the show. This leads me to tip number 65.

Tip 65: Supplement for Skin Care

For my show and breeding stock, there is one supplement that I use to manage the skincare of my hogs. I feed "Mini Pig Skin and Coat Supplement" by *Manna Pro,* made with flaxseed and other skin maintenance ingredients. I feed this to all my stock to take care of their skin and coat needs. I mix this in daily for their feed rations once per day. Each bag comes with a scoop that has two different-sized ends, and I often feed one of the larger scooped ends per day.

This has made a significant difference in the skincare of my hogs. The hair grows back in a few weeks after the supplement is strictly implemented for some of my sows who have had bald spots.

Supplements are crucial to the success of hogs because they have different health benefits and meet the varying needs of the pigs as they arise. However, even though they are extremely beneficial, they are not the only thing to consider. Along with the shampoos from the last section and the supplements for the different health needs, there are also ways to do the things listed in this chapter naturally.

How to Go Natural

For some individuals, the idea of filling their hogs full of chemicals is not an option or even worth considering. Those individuals often turn to natural remedies to meet their hog health needs. I have also personally turned to each of these methods at some point or another, which is why I feel comfortable including them in this chapter. The uses of these natural resources vary from overall health to stress to even alternatives for mild antibiotics. This first tip will be all the natural resources I recommend related to overall daily health.

Tip 66: Natural Remedies for Overall Health

A blend of natural foods that I feed to my stock each day includes a blend of papaya powder and banana chip powder. I make this myself by blending up banana chips and then mixing that with the papaya powder with a ratio of 1:1. This blend is beneficial for many reasons because papaya and banana have a multitude of health-related benefits for people and pigs. Bananas contain beneficial antioxidants and have properties that can help with muscle growth. This is beneficial for show stock to help them build appropriate muscle structure and keep the muscle relaxed rather than tense. Still, it is also helpful for breeding stock because as they get bigger and they get ready to labor, their muscles need to be in prime condition to deliver their litter. In addition, athletes have used bananas to prevent muscle cramping, which can be useful for both types of pig stock. Papaya, on the other hand, is very useful for gut health. As a child growing up, whenever I would get nervous or feel nauseous, I would eat a papaya tablet that would help get rid of nausea. Papaya is also very good for gut health, and I have noticed this with my hogs that I have fed papaya to. Mixing this blend together and adding it to their feed ration has made a difference in how they absorb the nutrients in their feed. Their overall appearance and health have improved because they are getting antioxidants and other nutrients beneficial to their health.

Homemade papaya and banana daily blend.

Tip 67: Natural Wormer

There are natural sources for a multitude of needs, including worming. If you are trying to prevent worms or you notice that your hog has worms and you want to treat them for it, you can use garlic or pomegranate to treat it naturally. Garlic is likely the easiest to acquire, which makes it the easiest to feed to your hogs for worming, and since pigs are not very picky eaters, it is likely that you could give them a few cloves, and they would still eat them. You can also use garlic powder instead and mix it into their feed ration. The pomegranate, if accessible, will likely be more appreciated by your pigs, as it is more palatable, and thus, they will like it more. However, both work, so whichever is accessible, will be a viable option for a natural dewormer for pigs.

Tip 68: Natural Antibiotic Aid

There isn't anything that can be used as a complete natural replacement when it comes to antibiotics. However, there are natural resources that can be used to help with antibiotic needs. For example, beets have properties that can help with mild infections without the use of antibiotics. Beets have blood cleansing and antioxidant properties, paired with anti-inflammatory benefits; it is the perfect mild infection remedy. After giving beets to a hog with an external infection in a small wound, the infection and the wound were healed within a week. Additionally, beets are highly palatable for pigs so that they will eat them with ease and no fuss.

Tip 69: Natural Skin Care

When it comes to skincare, there are some things you can give orally, such as flaxseed and anything high in vitamin C, but you can also use coconut oil as a type of moisturizer or topical conditioner that can aid in hair growth and softness, and skin moisturizer. Additionally, using aloe on their skin can help with skin and coat maintenance. However, please be sure not to use aloe as a feed additive because they are toxic to hogs and can cause diarrhea and nausea. In the summer, if you are using coconut oil, make sure that your hog has a place to be out of the sun, and you mix it with aloe or some other skin protectant because if in direct sun, the oil can cause sunburn to occur quickly.

Tip 70: Natural Probiotics Sources

If you have access to natural and raw dairy products, this is for you. Yogurt is high in probiotics and other fats and properties that are extremely beneficial to gut health in hogs. I would only give yogurt to them if it is natural because anything purchased from the store, while it is probably okay, there is a chance that some have an additive that pigs cannot have or that the pig has a reaction to the pasteurization. This is why I only feed my pigs natural dairy products from the farm.

If you don't have access to natural dairy products, you can still get a lot of properties, including probiotics, from pumpkin seeds. Pumpkin seeds are full of beneficial natural nutrients, antioxidants, and probiotics, making them a pig superfood. This can be implemented into a daily feed ration or as needed to meet the needs of all your pig stock.

Tip 71: Natural Weight and Muscle Gain

As stated above, I would only recommend these products if you have access to a dairy with raw products or have your own source of raw dairy products; however, if you do and would like to build muscle or fat in your hog, milk, and eggs are how to do it. Pigs will eat practically anything but eggs and milk, they love. You can even feed the shell to the pig if the egg is fresh to give them extra calcium for their structure. I feed these two foods to my show stock throughout their training and life because they are great muscle builders and are beneficial for a multitude of reasons, and I feed it at a ration to my breeding stock for the health properties related to both foods. It helps my sows with their muscle mass and staying fit for breeding, and the calcium from the eggshells helps keep their structure strong for longevity. I do caution not to feed too much dairy to breeding stock, though, because since it is high in fat, it can make them grow too big very quickly, making them less reliable for breeding. That being said, a portioned amount throughout the week is very beneficial for them.

Chapter Review:

- When it comes to pig skincare, shampoos and conditioners are crucial to soft skin and hair.
- Purple/whitening shampoo can remove and prevent any stains from occurring on your hogs that have white on them.
- Pink stuff mixed with pro polish is a great conditioner to use as a spray that will give your pig an edge with a shine in the show ring.
- For black hogs, show sheen gives them a slightly wet look that will attract the eye of the judge and help you rise to the top.
- When it comes to supplements, there is a multitude of options for any of your health-related pig needs; however, there are some that are more desired than others in each of the areas.
- For muscle building, I recommend "High Octane Fitter 25" for best results.
- When it comes to conditioning and fat cover, "Sumo" and "Chub it Up" are the best products and provide great results.
- For overall health, "Soft Silk," "Show Bloom," and "Fresh and Feminine" for females are the best products that will aid in muscle, fat, nutrient, and overall health needs.
- For mostly nutrient supplements, "Dyne" and "Equerry's Probiotics" are the products I use daily on my breeding and show stock.
- Supplements regarding skincare, "Mini Pig Skin and Coat" is the best I've used to maintain skincare in pigs.
- In stressful situations, "Show Eze" can be used to make events less stressful and relax your hogs to keep them show and travel-ready.
- There are a lot of alternative natural options for supplements and skincare such as coconut oil and aloe for skin, garlic and pomegranate for worms, beets for infections and wounds, papaya and banana for daily care, yogurt and pumpkin seeds for probiotics, and eggs and milk for weight and muscles.

Chapter 7: Illnesses to Be Aware of

As I have stated a couple of times, hogs are sensitive animals, vulnerable to many different illnesses and diseases. In this chapter, I will be reviewing the different illnesses and diseases to be aware of while raising your hogs; these range from respiratory illnesses, different health issues that are common and may arise, and even how to manage stress in pigs. I will also be covering how to take care of wounds on a hog.

Respiratory Illnesses

Pig lungs are vulnerable to a multitude of illnesses, and some are even transmittable to humans or other animals. For this reason, it is crucial to be aware of the different effects and how to manage hog health. Most of these illnesses can transform into a more significant issue, pneumonia, and can prove fatal. Maintaining strong biosecurity and a reliable vaccination schedule can prevent these illnesses from occurring. First, however, it is vital to know and understand how they work so that one can identify them and treat them properly.

Tip 72: Know How to Identify Strep

Strep is a very deadly and fast-moving illness in pigs. It is one of the most difficult to diagnose because the symptoms vary greatly. Anything from nausea to paralysis or from blindness to sudden death can all be symptoms of strep. Other symptoms include:

- Redness of the skin
- Depression

- Fatigue
- Fever
- Loss of appetite
- Paddling
- Shaking
- Convulsing
- Lameness

With all of these symptoms and sudden death in some circumstances, it can be extremely difficult to determine what illness is causing this to happen. However, once it is determined that the illness is strep, it can be treated with antibiotic injections.

The antibiotic that is recommended to use on pigs who have strep is called Excede. This antibiotic is very potent and strong, fighting against even the toughest of sicknesses and infections. This antibiotic can be obtained from Valley Vet Supply, an online resource for livestock and other pet needs. Along with injecting the infected pig with the Excede and following the dosage instructions, any infected hogs must be separated from the healthier ones to prevent it from spreading. It is crucial to act fast because strep spreads quickly. At the first sign of strep, hogs must be separated and treated to prevent any fatalities from happening. After that, it sets in quickly and transfers even quicker. The faster you are at identifying the problem and acting on it, the better the chance you have at keeping the rest of your herd safe.

It is difficult to prevent Strep from infecting a herd because it can be carried on clothes from people, or some pigs may also be a carrier, meaning they have the bacteria but are not affected by it. There is not a vaccine to prevent it in pigs, so the best way to keep your herd safe is through a biosecurity protocol that protects all hogs.

Tip 73: Swine Flu

Another type of respiratory illness that pigs can endure is the swine flu. This can be vaccinated against, unlike strep, which is valuable because this can be transmitted to humans from pigs. In order to prevent this from happening, one can purchase the FluSure pack on Valley Vet and inject this vaccination to prevent pigs from developing this illness. However, the vaccination is not a sure science, and it is still possible that the pigs will develop symptoms, which include:

- Fever
- Depression
- Coughing
- Discharge from nose and eyes
- Sneezing
- Loss of appetite

All of these are sure signs that there is a respiratory issue going on that needs to be addressed.

Once symptoms arise, it is vital to seclude the animal(s) affected and keep them quarantined until symptoms are gone. One way to keep them from getting worse and help them get better would be to give their hogs a dose of LA200 or Penicillin once a day for three days. Following the dosage directions on the bottle, the pig should be on the mend within a couple of days after the first dose. It is important to keep the hog away from the rest of the herd until symptoms surpass, just in case it is still contagious, and to prevent it from spreading. Additionally, sanitizing hands and using proper precautions when a pig is sick with swine flu can help prevent it from being transmitted to you as well.

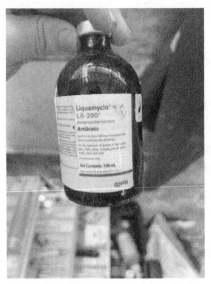

Bottle of LA-200 injection.

With these two respiratory issues, if left untreated, they can transform into pneumonia, which is a much more serious illness.

Tip 74: Treating Pneumonia

When a pig comes down with pneumonia, the symptoms are similar to those of strep and the flu, but they are more severe. Some of the symptoms that are higher in severity include:

- Coughing
- Depression
- Loss of appetite
- Fatigue
- Runny Nose

If you start to notice that your hog is developing these symptoms and has an aggressive dry cough, they may have pneumonia. The first step should be to separate your hog from any other pigs that may be around. While pneumonia itself may not still be contagious, whatever caused the pneumonia could still be contagious, so it is important to quarantine the pig until they are feeling better. This also gives the hog an opportunity to rest without the stress of being around the other hogs. The next step would be to treat the pneumonia with three days of LA200 or Penicillin. Either one of these drugs will be effective in treating the pneumonia. Ensuring that the hog has access to plenty of water, room to rest, and stays on feed will be crucial to their recovery.

Internal Issues Turned External

While respiratory issues are common, they are not the only illnesses that pigs may face. In this next section, we will be covering prolapses and hernias. These conditions are issues where internal organs and parts come out, and they can cause a multitude of issues down the line.

Tip 75: How to Treat a Prolapse

There are two kinds of prolapses that are common: anal/rectal and vaginal/uterine. This condition can occur in any species of livestock and, depending on the severity, can be easily treated and taken care of.

In anal prolapses, the rectum is pushed outside the body, causing a bulge to appear at the anus. When this occurs, if it is small enough, one could simply gently coax the prolapse back into the anus and use a pocket stitch to help prevent it from happening again. In some more severe cases, it may be necessary to contact a vet to do a small procedure that will cause the prolapsed portion of the rectum to fall off and detach itself, solving the problem. It takes inserting a corrugated tube into the lumen of the rectum. Then a rubber band should be placed over the prolapse as close as possible to the perineal skin.

In some cases, the prolapse may be able to move down the tube, but most of the time, it blocks the tube. However, this has not proven to be an issue because the prolapse tends to detach in 5-7 days. While not immediately fatal, if led untreated, anal prolapses may lead to the rectum dying or severe infection, leading to the pig's death.

The other type of prolapse that is possible is uterine prolapse. This is often only seen in older sows, who have been bred several times. However, it is not impossible to see this condition in younger females. Vaginal prolapses occur when the uterus is strained and thus exits the vagina, most commonly during intense or active labor, in older sows who either have a very large litter or a litter of very large piglets. When this occurs, the easiest option is to try and gently coax the uterus back inside the sow where it belongs. To do this, one would need to apply lube to their hand to make insertion easier, and then using one hand, they would push and manipulate the uterus back into the sow. The sow this happens to will likely need to be culled because chances are, it will occur again. If there are still piglets inside when this occurs, promptly remove them to prevent them from asphyxiating and dying inside the sow. If it is a severe case of uterine prolapse, it may be necessary to call a vet for professional help; however, in most cases, the sow either dies from internal hemorrhages or is culled for welfare reasons. Thus, the best option would be to save as many piglets from the sow as possible and cull her.

Tip 76: Know How to Treat Hernias

Another type of condition where parts that are supposed to remain internal become external is a hernia. There are a few different types of hernias in hogs, such as umbilical, scrotal, and inguinal. Scrotal and inguinal are similar in how they occur; however, inguinal hernias can occur in females as well, so it is important to distinguish between the two.

As the name suggests, umbilical hernias are hernias that occur in the umbilical cord, often closely after the piglet is born. The majority of these hernias are caused by infection of the umbilical cord and when connective tissue fails to close around the umbilical ring. In order to treat this, one must obtain elastrator rings. Similar to banding, these rings get stretched over the hernia, and it cuts off blood flow, causing the herniated umbilical cord to detach. This technique seems to solve the problem. While umbilical hernias are not always this way, it is important to note that they can be hereditary. This would mean that either the sow or the boar passed it on to the litter of piglets. This may become evident if there are several piglets from a litter with this condition.

Another type of hernia is a scrotal hernia. I have seen these most often when castrating a piglet. This occurs when the tissues weaken, and due to this, the internal organs make their way into the scrotum through a small hole. This type of hernia is easiest to treat when the piglets are young. This is because the hole isn't as large, and neither are the organs. While castrating, if you notice organs in the scrotum that are not testicles or any other reproductive parts, the first thing you should do is hold the piglet up by their hind legs to prevent the hernias from getting any worse or coming out any farther. After the piglet is held this way, one needs to gently use fingers to coax the organs back into place inside the piglet. After this is done (both testicles should be removed at this point), spray with iodine or vetericyn, and using vet wrap or some other type of bandage tape or wrap, make an infinity sign around the piglet's legs, 'figure-eighting' to cover the incision. This should not only protect the wound but also keep the organs in place, preventing them from exiting the body. Once the incision is healed, it should be alright to remove the bandage, and the hernia will also likely be healed.

For other inguinal hernias, especially in females, where castration is not done, surgical repair is required if the hog is going to be used for breeding purposes such as a gilt or a boar. If the hog is strictly for show or market purposes unless the hernia is extremely large and should be treated right away, it can be left until after the show or until the hog is butchered. If the hernia is being treated by surgery, the vet will gently push the organs back where they belong and do a small stitch in the weak abdomen wall to prevent it from reoccurring.

When internal organs and parts start to exit the body and end up on the outside, this is not an ideal situation. However, pigs also have external and neurological conditions that occur that may need to be treated as well. This leads to the next section, which speaks about the external wounds and abscesses that hogs may face.

External Conditions and Their Treatment

In this section of chapter seven, I will be talking about how to treat and take care of wounds in hogs and how to treat an abscess if it occurs. Both of these situations are very plausible to occur, so it is important to be prepared in case they do.

Tip 77: How to Treat Wounds

When it comes to any type of animal, wound care can be difficult because they don't comprehend that keeping the bandage on will help them heal. Any wraps or bandages often don't stay on, and if hogs are in large groups, they may pick on each other's wounds, causing them to get worse or potentially get infected. So, if you notice that one of your hogs has a wound that needs to be treated, the first step is to separate the hog from the rest of the herd. This ensures that the other hogs don't mess with the wound or attack the wounded pig. Then, once the hog is separated, it is important to analyze the wound to determine the severity. Determine how deep it is, what may have caused it, and what the next course of action may be. I always use vetericyn on the wounds of my livestock; even at times, I use it for myself. It has incredible healing properties that keep a wound from getting infected and ensures it heals quickly. I spray this generously on the wound until it is completely covered. Depending on the location and the severity of the wound, this may be the only necessary step. If you believe the wound should be protected to prevent dirt or debris from getting inside, you can either use a mild sealant to protect it or use a bandage/wrap to cover it up. It would be difficult to use a wrap or bandage on the wound if it is located on the back or other larger area, as the bandage would not likely stay on very easily, so leave that up to your judgment of the location and severity. In those cases where the wound needs to be protected but cannot be covered, it is possible to use a cream of sorts to protect it from the elements. One product I often use to prevent dirt and debris from getting into wounds in hard-to-wrap places is Vaseline or coconut oil. Coconut oil would also help the skin heal quickly, but Vaseline works well for protecting the wound, especially if the hog cannot be separated from the rest of the pigs.

Bottle of normal spray on vetericyn

Another product that can be used on a wound to help it to heal quickly would be fresh aloe vera. Aloe has healing and moisturizing properties that could assist with the healing factor of the wound. Applying some once a day could greatly increase the chances of the wound healing quickly and prevent any scars from occurring, as it protects and treats the skin as well.

Tip 78: Identifying and Treating an Abscess

Abscesses are collections of pus and debris under the skin. These often appear as a small to large bulge under the pig's skin in a multitude of possible areas. When they first form, abscesses are often hard, possibly hot, to the touch. It is at this point that you want to leave it alone. To help with the heat, you could run cold water on it from the faucet, but it cannot be drained until it is soft.

Once the abscess either ruptures on its own or is soft enough to drain, you can take a larger needle (16-14 gauge) to poke a hole. Once the hole is poked, the abscess should start to drain out of that hole. However, if it does not, it may be necessary to use a scalpel and make a small incision to allow the drainage to go out. Then once it starts to drain, you may apply slight pressure to the bulge, encouraging it and squeezing the contents out. This may take some time, depending on the size of the abscess. Once you believe you have gotten all of the contents out, fill a syringe with hydrogen peroxide, and inject it into the hole you drained the abscess from. This will clear out any remaining contents and prevent infection in the future. You could also use warm water to clean it out. Then after this, give an antibiotic for three days (LA 200, Excede, or Penicillin) and spray the hole or incision with vetericyn. This will prevent any infection from occurring and help your hog heal promptly.

One condition is becoming more and more common in hogs, especially show hogs, that can have external and internal effects. Stress conditions are popping up more and more, and some have been proven to be linked to genetics. In this next tip, I will discuss one of the conditions pigs may face and how to limit stress in your breeding and show stock.

Tip 79: Dippity Pig Syndrome

Stress is becoming more of an issue, especially when selecting which sows and boars to use and what hogs to show. Whether this is due to the intense breeding to get the desired high muscle appearance or cross-breeding, it's hard to say, but it is more prevalent, meaning the chances of having an encounter with a pig with stress issues is higher than before. One that is especially serious is called 'Dippity Pig Syndrome".

While other stress issues may just cause your hog to be agitated easier or have a purple tint to their skin after working for extended periods of time, Dippity Pig has much more severe and intense symptoms. Dippity Pig is identifiable by the sores or wounds that appear laterally on the pig's back, paralysis or stiffness of the hind legs and lower back, squealing in pain, dragging hind legs on the ground, and going off of feed. If you notice all of these signs simultaneously or at the same time, your hog is likely suffering from Dippity Pig Syndrome. While there is no cure for it, there are some remedies that I have developed and have proven to be effective in at least limiting or making the symptoms less severe.

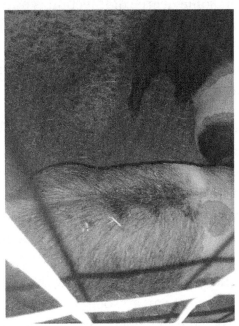

Dippity pig syndrome lateral sores on the back of an affected hog.

One thing that I have used and noticed that has a positive effect on the symptoms is blending papaya and banana together. The papaya soothes the stomach, making the pig less stressed and more likely to continue eating without losing an appetite. The banana has qualities that help with muscle cramps. When the back and hindlegs tense up during an episode, it is similar to a muscle cramp. I have found that banana helps soothe the muscles, making this side effect less intense or severe. Another item that I use frequently is a natural caffeine resource that is okay for pigs to eat. I use natural ones when treating a potential breeding stock, but other caffeine sources work well for regular show stock. In the past, Mt. Dew has proven to work well in settling the mind. Similar to an individual with ADHD, caffeine helps balance the pig's brain with their body, making it easy to manage and calm down when needed. For the wounds, I typically use vetericyn and some sealant to prevent infection; however, some degree of infection is often inevitable. Due to this, I often turn to beets to prevent or treat any infections. Beets are blood cleaners and also anti-inflammatories, so they help with overall wound care. They are also highly palatable, making them an easy solution to feeding your hog for infections.

Something important to note and remember when it comes to Dippity Pig is that if a hog is having an episode, do not interfere or push them to keep walking or moving. They are often in very intense pain, preventing them from moving or functioning properly, so patience and respect are key. Another thing to note is that hogs with Dippity Pig likely should not be used as breeding stock. It wouldn't be humane to breed these hogs with all of the stresses that go into breeding and the chances of passing the stress on to offspring. They may go into an episode while delivering a litter of hogs, which could be fatal or catastrophic in that situation. It is best to decide that if a hog shows signs of stress disorders, they should be culled or sold rather than kept in the herd.

Chapter Review:

- The main respiratory illnesses seen in hogs are strep, flu, and pneumonia.
- In almost all instances, antibiotics are needed to either prevent infection, treat illness, or treat an existing infection.
- It is crucial to develop and maintain a strong biosecurity protocol, complete with hog quarantine, disinfectant of clothes and new hogs or tools, and separation from the herd when necessary.
- Prolapses and hernias are situations in which organs that are supposed to be internal either exit the body or go to a place where they are not supposed to be.
- Hernias and prolapses need to be treated promptly to prevent infections or fatality.
- When it comes to wound care, it is essential to keep the wound clean, sprayed with vetericyn, and protected from debris or dirt.
- Be sure to drain an abscess when it is soft to prevent the infection from spreading into the bloodstream.
- As breeding continues the way it is going, stress conditions increase and worsen. It is important to know the signs and be prepared with remedies to assist with the symptoms and side effects.

Chapter 8: Everything About Pig Shows

When it comes to showing your pigs, there is a lot to prepare for and things to do prior to attending the show, and then after that, the show is packed full of activities, and things move quickly, so it is important to be prepared. From joining a group to show with to getting you and your pig ready, and then actually showing, there are a lot of steps that need to be broken down and will be in this chapter.

Deciding Where to Show

While a lot of the steps in this section should be decided before you even get your hogs, they have to do with the show and how you prepare, so this is why they are listed here.

Tip 80: Deciding on a Show

There are three primary types of shows that can be attended: fair, jackpot, and pig show. While all of these have pig showing, they have different qualities that impact the choices some individuals may make about what shows to attend and what club you may want to join. Fairs are typically the more laid-back option unless you attend a state fair. They consist of a market class and a fitting and showing class. Then, some fairs also have a round-robin where Grand and Reserve in each livestock class compete in all the different livestock classes and try to win overall showmen. Finally, fairs also have a sale on the final day, where showmen can sell their livestock in an auction.

Jackpots are higher stakes than fairs, but they are mostly for practice and building connections in the showman industry. Jackpots are put on across the country to practice showing your animal and see how they would do in a showing event. These are higher stakes because often, there are buckles and banners associated with winning, and the showmen who attend jackpots are often more experienced, making the pool of competition denser. The difference between fairs and jackpots is that there isn't often a sale or auction at the end where showmen get rid of their hogs. This is one of the reasons that jackpots are best known for practice because the showmen don't have to sell their show hog after. These are also places to put your work on display. Breeders will attend jackpots and show their hogs to show off their genetics, breeding abilities, and training/showing practice as well. These shows, like the fairs, also have a market and a fitting and showing class; however, in the larger jackpots, the market class will be divided up by breed rather than having breeds mixed. This doesn't work for the smaller shows, but it evens the playing field and helps to display the different qualities of the breeds in the larger jackpots.

The other primary type of show is just livestock shows, and they are at the national or regional level. These are very high-stakes shows that happen all over the nation. One of the biggest ones happens to be "Arizona Nationals." At these shows, showmen truly put their skills to the test, showing against the best of the best in the nation. Additionally, at these types of shows, big breeding operations such as "Shipley Swine Genetics" purchase their prospect boars or breeding gilts. At these shows, boars are allowed to be shown when normally male hogs need to be castrated. There are often auctions at the end of shows, but in some of the higher-stake ones, only a certain number of showmen can sell their pigs. This is typically determined based on placing in the market class. While not recommended for first-time showmen, these shows offer an experience that, if possible, is recommended to experience at some point in a showman's career.

Once you have decided what type of show you wish to attend, you then need to research the shows in the area and determine what your options are. Between 4H and FFA, there are different types of shows they offer and attend. There are also independent programs and organizations that are available if you wish to go that route.

Tip 81: Pick an Organization or Group

When it comes to showing, one can either be associated with an organization or group or go through a more independent and open approach for shows. There are three options available: 4H, FFA, or open. Each of these has different requirements and perks of being associated with them.

4H typically is where people get started with showing. This organization allows younger children to show animals at fairs and sometimes jackpots. They typically don't go to the bigger shows that are regional or national level, so there are some limitations in that standpoint. Sometimes there are 4H groups that don't even go to jackpots. This is similar to FFA; however, FFA is only for high school students, and they typically stick to fairs, and that is it. 4H and FFA are best known for attending state and county fairs, and that is mostly it. The main difference between 4H and FFA is the age difference and how you get associated with them. 4H is independently run by small groups in communities, typically by parents who have children that want to show. FFA is an organization associated with high school, which is why you have to be old enough (in high school) to join, while 4H is anyone from about 5-18.

If you want to attend jackpots and the bigger shows, you will likely have to be associated with an independent organization such as 509 or show in open classes as an independent showman. I have never worked with these organizations, so I have no experience with how they work, but these types of showmen have more freedom regarding which shows they would like to attend and where in the country they would like to go. 4H and FFA tend to stick to no larger than the state level, sometimes even only ones that are in the area. FFA is only able to attend the fairs in their area because they only receive a certain amount of funding to attend shows. This puts limitations on the shows they are able to attend. 4H groups have more leniency because since they are typically family-run, it is more based on what the families can afford for stall fees, traveling, and registration costs. However, if you register as an open or independent showman, then you will have even more freedom on which shows to attend.

Deciding which shows to attend greatly affects what group you will join. Once you have decided which show you are going to, you can research groups in your area and decide if you would like to do 4H, FFA if you are old enough, or if you want to do independent showing through a higher organization. After deciding all of these factors, you can start to prepare for the show as it gets closer.

How to Prepare

Pig shows can be intense, so knowing how to properly prepare and get yourself and your hog ready is key to your success. In the weeks leading up to the show, your hog needs to be groomed, training needs to increase in intensity, and you will need to collect all the gear and materials you need to be successful at the show.

Tip 82: Proper Grooming is Key

Grooming is necessary to make your hog look its best, to maintain that fitted and finished look. To get to this point, simply washing your pig every day and brushing them frequently won't be enough. A couple of weeks before the show, you will need to use clippers to trim their hair to an appropriate length in different areas.

To train the hair and get your hogs used to being brushed, you should brush them every day for a few minutes to keep them clean, train their hair to go the correct way, and also get them used to being brushed. Yet, as it gets closer to the show, you will need to trim their hair in certain areas. Clipping your hog will give them the show pig look, and the eye appeal judges look for. The focus of your clipping should be along the edges of the ears to make the long hairs even and clipping the body if the hair is long, especially if you are bringing your hog to spring shows. Through the winter months, your hogs will likely develop a thicker and longer hair, which in the show ring, while not unappealing, would look better if it were trimmed to be a uniform 2-3 inches in length. Avoid trimming the tail and legs, although it may be tempting to do so. The leg hair can help make the legs look thicker, giving the appearance of having a thicker bone structure. A thicker tail (as long as it is docked) will also help to give an illusion of a thicker and wider ham. Other than this, your pig's hair should be trimmed to be even. Clippers often come with or have guards available that prevent the blade from cutting too close or too short. This is recommended because, especially if you are within a couple of weeks of the show, it is better to have hair that is a little too long than to have hair that is too short. You can always go a little shorter, but once the length is cut off, you cannot add that length back, just hope it grows back enough by the time it is time to show.

Preparing for the show also includes intense training in the weeks leading up to ensure your hog is ready for the ring. This leads me to the next tip.

Tip 83: Intensely Train the Weeks Leading Up to the Show

Throughout your hog's training, they have built up stamina that allows them to drive longer; they have learned patience, how to drive their head at an appropriate length, and how to trust you as the showman. In the weeks leading up to the show, you should push the boundaries of your hog's showing abilities and try different strategies and tricks with them. By this point, your hog should trust you enough to follow your guidance through obstacles, driving back and forth, driving towards you, driving to the left or right in front of you. Additionally, since their stamina should be built up, by this point, your hog should be able to drive for 15+ minutes with ease. It would be ideal to drive them for 15 minutes at least once a day, preferably twice a day, to get them ready for the show. At the show, you may be asked to enter the ring more than once on the same day, sometimes an hour or so between each time. This occurs when you get pulled for the champion rounds. Driving your hog for at least this long, setting up obstacles to test their listening skills and stamina, will get them ready for the show ring.

Training my market barrow before the show.

When you are in the show ring, especially for the fitting and showing class, you may be asked to do things to show how well your hog has been trained and listens to you. For example, you may be asked to walk your hog over a line in shavings, touch their nose to a certain spot, or have them walk over a board. In addition, you may be asked to walk to a specific corner, put your hog in a smaller pen by walking through a closed gate, close the gate behind you, or even stop your hog and keep them standing still. For this reason, you need to be prepared and prepare your hog for anything they may face in the show ring.

Proper grooming and training are essential, but after those bases are covered, you need to pack for the show and get all of your tools and necessities in order and ready to go.

Tip 84: Creating a Proper Packing List

When you are at the show, you don't want to realize that you don't have everything you need in your tack box. When I prepare my materials and tools for the show, I often make a list extremely similar to this a couple of days before the show starts. You will want to make sure you have:

- Water sprayer
- Your shampoos
- Your conditioners and sprays
- A small brush for in the show ring
- A larger brush for before the show
- Another brush for washing
- Baby wipes
- Clippers
- Extension cord
- Enough grain to last the duration of the show
- Extra bales of shavings just in case
- Feed pans
- A few buckets
- A tote to carry wash-rack materials
- Your whips
- A staple gun
- A few miscellaneous tools (hammer, screwdriver, etc.)
- Screws
- Nails
- Zip ties
- Your show clothes (FFA gear, or professional show wear)
- Muck boots for the wash-rack
- Collapsible hose (some shows don't have hoses)
- Pitchfork and shovel
- Wheelbarrow
- Sharpies
- Broom

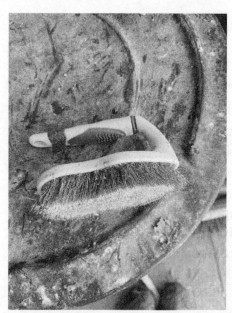

The small brush I used in the show ring

Sprayer tool for leading up to the show ring, training, or giving your hog a drink before you enter the ring.

All of the things on this list are items that I have used at least once at a show, most of them I have used at each one. You will have to maintain a clean space, ensure that all of the things around your pen are in tip-top shape, and you will also need to make sure you have everything you need to take care of your hog while at the show. You never know when you will need a tool to fix something that breaks, so having a few tools on hand to do minor fixes is a good idea. It is recommended that you get a chest or tack box to put all of your materials in to keep all of these items in one place. I built a standing tack box, and it contains all of the tools and materials that I need, except for the shovel, pitchfork, broom, and wheelbarrow. Everything else fits inside and locks to ensure no one steals any of my gear. If you don't wish to build your own, you can purchase ones of different styles and varieties to meet your needs.

An old tack box built to hold all of my gear.

While At the Show

When you are at the show, there will be a lot going on and a lot on your mind at the same time. In this section, I will be covering everything to be prepared for and expect when you are at the show. This section is more related to fairs at different levels. Jackpots and other livestock shows may vary, but this is accurate with what to expect when it comes to fairs.

Tip 85: Maintaining a Clean Area

At a show, you are judged not only on how well you show and the physique of your hog but also on how well you maintain an area to be proud of. This means cleaning your stall each day and spot cleaning throughout the rest of the day as well. Using a broom, you will also need to sweep in front of your stall to keep the walkways clean and clear for guests visiting the show. Judges will come through and analyze each stall to ensure cleanliness is being held to the highest of standards and maintained. The pitchfork is best for spot cleaning anything your pig does throughout the day, and the shovel is best used for clearing out the entire stall when necessary. There will be a designated area to dump dirty shavings using the wheelbarrow. Some shows provide shavings; however, others do not, or the shavings they provide are cedar and cause allergic reactions. For this reason, I often bring my own shavings just in case they are necessary. If you keep a routine of cleaning the entire pen each morning if it is needed and spot cleaning throughout the day, you will receive high marks for having a well-maintained area.

Tip 86: Market Class

Often the first class you will show in will be a market class. In fairs, this is only divided up by weight. So, the heaviest pigs will show against each other, and the lightest pigs will show against each other. They may also separate the classes up by breed in other shows, and only specific breeds will show against each other. This evens the playing field a little, but you won't often see this done in normal fairs at the local level. Those that place high in the first round will move onto the champion round. At the fair level, this will include all the breeds and a mixture of different weights. At the higher level, with breeds separated, the breeds will still be separated, but now all the weights for each of those breeds will show against each other. The second round is often the champion round to determine the best hog based on the physique.

It is this part of the hog show that the judge will focus on the structure of your hog, their muscle density, fat finish, and how they drive. In market, the goal is to determine which hog would rear the best quality of meat and hang the best carcass. While still important for impressions, this part of the show focuses less on how well your pig is behaving and how you show and more on how your pig looks and its productivity.

Showing in the market class at a county fair

Tip 87: Breeding Class

In this class, all of the rules and processes are the same as the market; however, the goal isn't to hang a carcass but to actually produce more show hogs. In this class, you can show gilts, or even sometimes boars, to be judged based on their structure, build, and productivity to be a breeding prospect. Breeding hogs need to have longevity, while market hogs only need to last till butcher, so the goal in this class is to determine which gilt or boar would be the best candidate to produce show quality hogs for years to come. At local fairs, all breeds are shown against each other, and it isn't very often that boars are present mostly gilts. However, boars are more prominent at jackpots and higher-level hog shows and fairs, and gilts may be separated to show against the same breed.

Tip 88: Fitting & Showing

The next major part of pig shows and fairs is the fitting and showing class. In this class, even at the higher level, all breeds are shown against each other because the focus is less on the structure of the hog and more on how well trained the hog is and how well you work as a team with your pig. They do differentiate between experience level and age for the first round, so the new showmen aren't going to show against the showmen who have been at it their entire lives right off the get-go. This makes the first round more even for all of the showmen in the ring.

In this class, the primal focus is your hog's behavior and receptiveness to guidance and how well you know how to show off your hog while watching the judge. Your goal will be to keep your hog moving in front of the judge and keep them between you and the judge. Avoid touching the judge by controlling your hog's nose and direction wisely. As the stakes get higher, there will be more challenges that the judge will give you, such as putting your hog into a smaller pen, making them touch their nose to a certain spot, walking over a line or board, or walking in a certain pattern. The judge may also ask you questions about your hog in this class, such as "what is their best feature?" "How much weight has your hog gained since you purchased it?" This tests your knowledge and you as a showman regarding attention to detail.

Me showing my grand champion breeding gilt in the fitting and showing class.

For all of the classes, you should go in with a hog that is clean and looking its best; however, it is most crucial in fitting and showing because you will be judged distinctly on how well your hog is maintained. Additionally, just like the other classes, there will be a first round where you are separated by experience. Then there will be a final round where all finalizing showmen are in the ring together, showing for the champion title.

Tip 89: Round Robin

After the winner for fitting and showing is determined, the "Reserve" and "Grand Champion" showmen will get the opportunity to show all of the other livestock. This is a tradition at larger fairs to determine the overall showman. The top two showmen from each livestock group will be brought into a "Round Robin" competition to determine who deserves the title of a top showman. Each showman will need to demonstrate their skills showing cattle, sheep, meat goats, yard goats, swine, and sometimes even horses. Depending on the area, cattle may include dairy and beef cattle. For example, if you are one of the top showmen from swine, you will not need to show swine again because you have demonstrated your skills already. Instead, you will bring your hog to the show ring, and the corresponding showman with your level will show your stock in each round.

After completing each of the rounds, the showmen will put away their stock in their rightful stalls, and then after the judges have come to an agreement based on scores from each round, the top two overall livestock showmen will be determined. This is a great opportunity for showmen to practice showing different species of livestock and determining who has a showing skill set that can be applied across the board.

Tip 90: Market Sale/Auction

At the end of the show, mostly larger shows and fairs, there will be a livestock sale where showmen can sell their stock to buyers in the area. It is important leading up to this point to talk to the buyers before the auction to get your name out there and get them interested in buying your hog. It would even be helpful to send out support letters to local businesses and buyers in the area that will be attending the sale. These businesses sometimes send money to help prepare for the show, and they could also commit to purchasing your hog at the sale. It is smart to have a couple of buyers interested and lined up for you at the auction because otherwise, you are at the mercy of the sale and could get a low price for your hog. The more you market and reach out about your hog, the higher the price you may receive for your hog in the auction.

After the sale is finished, when the sale is over, your hog will go either to the home that purchased it or the butcher that the buyer is sending it to. Not all shows have a sale at the end, and not all hogs need to go through the sale. Unless you showed the hog in the market class, it is not eligible to go through the auction. Breeding stock (unless it is in a higher show, they may have a breeding stock auction) does not have to be sold and can be taken home at the end of the show. Jackpots also don't have auctions or sales at the end because this type of show is generally just for practicing before the real deal.

Chapter Review:

- You will need to decide which show(s) you would like to attend.
- Depending on which type of show you wish to attend, you will need to decide what group to join after conducting some research.
- While preparing for the show, you will need to trim and groom your hog with clippers and brushing weeks before the show.

- Preparing for the show, you will need to put your hog through intense training to get them ready for the obstacles they may face in the ring.
- Create a packing list of all your materials and gear you may need so that you are prepared for the show.
- While at the show, you will need to maintain your area by cleaning it daily.
- There will be a market class where your hog is judged based on physique
- There will be a fitting and showing class where your hog is judged based on training and overall cleanliness and appearance.
- If the show practices this, there will be a round-robin to test and determine who will be the titled as a top overall showman for all species of livestock.
- At the end of the show, there may be a sale where buyers purchase your hog through an auction-based on price per pound.

Chapter 9: Putting Meat in the Freezer

After the show, you may decide to take your hog home to put in your own freezer, or you may have hogs that you raised just to put meat on the table. In order to do this, you will need to know when your hog is ready for the freezer and what cuts of meat there are available on the pig. In this chapter, you will learn how to determine when your hog is ready for the freezer and what they can provide for the freezer.

How to Know They are Ready

There are different factors to consider when determining if your hog is ready for butcher and putting in the freezer; from age, weight, and appearance, there are many different things to consider when raising a hog for the freezer. In this section, you will learn about all of the things that will show you that your hog is ready for its final purpose.

Tip 91: Keep Track of Your Hog's Age

Most hogs are ready for butcher when they are about 6-8 months old. This is primarily the case when the hog has been intended for the freezer and has been on a diet to accommodate for this. If a hog was intended for other purposes and it was last minute determined to be for the freezer, they may need to be a little older. Still, typically, it is at this age that they reach their full capacity for muscle and start to finish with a fat cover.

Tip 92: Keep Track of Your Hog's Weight

The majority of hogs are butcher ready when they are around 280 pounds. This is why the minimum to the maximum weight for shows is from 230-290 pounds. This is generally the weight that hogs are when they have the amount of muscle they can sustain and the fat cover to balance it out. Some larger structured and bigger boned hogs may be able to maintain a higher weight so that they may weigh more; however, even the larger hogs are finished around this weight.

Tip 93: When a Pig Looks Ready

With weight and age not being an exact science for when your hog is ready for the butcher, it is always good to know how a hog should look when it is ready for the butcher. When you are raising a hog, the key thing to watch for when determining when your hog is ready for butcher is the fat cover. You don't want the fat to be too thick, but just enough to make the meat softer and more enjoyable. When your pig appears to be softer and has a tender touch (when you press on them, they are softer, less muscular, or firm), this could be a sure sign that your hog is ready for butcher. However, if your hog doesn't have the muscle to yield meat, then they are not ready for butcher and could benefit from some more time on grain to fill out. Without any muscle, there wouldn't be any meat to harvest from the hog. Ultimately to determine by appearance when your hog is ready for the freezer, there needs to be an even softening fat finish over a full muscular build.

Two images of hogs that are near ready to be butchered are two images. The hog on the left is ready, while the hog on the right needs more time to develop an appropriate fat cover.

What You Can Get from Hogs

Upon butchering a hog, one must know what to harvest from them and the different cuts of meat to focus on in the meat shop. There are different types of products that one can harvest from hogs, such as byproducts, meat, and even organs harvested for different purposes. In this section, all of the different products that can be harvested from pigs will be covered and talked about.

Tip 94: Know the Cuts of Meat

There are many prime cuts of meat that can be harvested from hogs, and it is important for anyone who is raising hogs for their own freezer to know what meat is best. The most popular ones are ham, bacon, and pork chops, but there are a few other ones that are important to know as well. This tip will cover all of those types of meat.

The ham is the rump of the hog and easily one of the most well-known cuts of meat. This needs to be cured and brined after being cut, so it is best to either have practice with that or send your hog to a shop for the ham. Another cut of meat that needs to be brined and cured is the bacon. Bacon is the belly of the hog, also known at times as pork belly. These two types of meat are the most well-known associated with hogs, and both need to be cured and brined after butchering.

Pork chops are another popular cut of meat on a hog. This cut of meat is located mostly along the back and can be collected from the loin on a hog. Pork chops are often tender due to fat content. The rest of the loin on a pig is another cut of meat that is often collected Not to be confused with the pork tenderloin, which is below the loin, and, as the name suggests, is much more tender and juicy. Tenderloin is a much more favored cut of meat and sells for a higher price than normal pork loin.

Another area where cuts of meat can be collected is the shoulder. In the shoulder region, the "Boston butt" and what's known as the picnic ham can be collected. These are larger cuts of meat that can be used for larger gatherings. An additional larger cut of meat comes from the ribs. Spareribs and regular ribs come from the side of the hog. These tend to have a decent fat cover on the outside, making the meat tender and juicy.

With the rest of the hog, any left-over meat can be used for sausage or ground pork. Similar to ground beef, ground pork can be used fo burgers, pastas, tacos, etc., and can be a mixture of left-over meats that can't be used otherwise. Likewise, sausage is similar to ground pork because any left-over meat can be used. Still, sausage is different in its process because spices often get added to give them different flavors, get stored in different casings, and often be smoked for flavor.

With all these different uses for the meat, one may be left wondering what to do with the rest of the hog. Although it may seem strange to some, even some organs can be used for cooking purposes.

Tip 95: Know What Organs are Harvestable

The two most popular organs used for cooking are the heart and the liver. Both of these organs get used in meals and cooked down as meat to get more use out of the whole hog. These organs tend to be tougher, however, so one will likely need to mix them with something soft and tender and in a way that prevents the organs from becoming too tough to eat. Hearts and livers can be used in stews, soups, or even with mixed vegetables. Another popular use of liver is liver and onions with a mixture of bacon and sometimes cabbage.

Another organ that can be used for different purposes is the intestine. For example, intestines are often used as casing for sausage, so they are collected. A lot of different cultures will do this themselves, but if one taught themselves how to turn the intestines into sausage casing, they could collect and save the hog intestines to do this.

Aside from organs and meat for cooking, there are other products that can be collected from the hog for other purposes. These byproducts are mostly for being fed to dogs, but some could also be used for human consumption.

Tip 96: Hog Byproducts

The main byproducts that one can collect from a butchered hog are nose, ears, and hooves. The hooves can be either fed to dogs or used to make pickled pigs' feet, a southern treat. Likewise, the ears and snout can be dried or fried as a treat for dogs.

There are also countless other uses for the bones, skin, and other extra parts of a hog that were not listed in this tip. However, the ones that are listed are the most common uses of byproducts from hogs and would likely be the easiest to use and master.

Chapter Review:

- Hogs are generally ready for butcher at around 6-8 months old
- A hog is ready for butcher around 280-300 pounds.
- When a hog is ready to put in the freezer, they will be full of muscle and have an even softening layer of fat finish to tenderize the muscles.
- The most commonly collected cuts of meat from a hog are ham, bacon, ribs, tenderloin and loin, picnic ham (shoulder), Boston butt, pork chops, sausages, and ground pork.
- The organs that can be easily harvested and used are the heart, liver, and intestines.
- Byproducts that are often harvested are the hooves (for cooking or dog consumption), ears, and snout. The snout and ears are used to make dog treats.

Chapter 10: Top 10 Most Frequently Asked Questions

With all of the information covered in the previous chapters, it is important to cover the most frequently asked questions about hogs to ensure that prime information that previously may not have been touched gets covered. Therefore, in this chapter, I will cover the top ten most frequently asked questions about pig care and other topics.

Tip 97: What is the gestational period of a sow length, and how many piglets does she have?

Sows typically have a gestational period of 114 days after conception, and the average litter size is 8-12 piglets.

Tip 98: How much do piglets weigh when they are born?

When piglets are born, they typically weigh between 2-4 pounds. Average, and healthy, is three pounds.

Tip 99: How old are piglets when they are weaned?

It depends on the breeder. I wean my piglets at three weeks, but some breeders may wean later than this, depending on preference.

Tip 100: Are pigs given hormones?

It is illegal to give pigs hormones for growth. Oxytocin can be used to encourage a sow that is in labor, but steroids of any type cannot be used for pigs in any way.

Tip 101: Are pigs given antibiotics?

Antibiotics are used to treat infections in hogs, but farmers must follow strict withdrawal periods for antibiotics and only use antibiotics when necessary. In addition, antibiotics must be cleared out of the system a certain number of days before butchering to ensure it is not in the meat.

Tip 102: What do pigs eat?

Most farms and farmers feed grain to their hogs that are a blend of primarily corn or soybean meal. In addition, other additives to the grain are mixed to add vitamins, minerals, or other nutrients.

Pig feed that is in the ground and dry form.

Tip 103: Are pigs raised by factory farms?

Family farms raise almost all of the pigs raised in the country.

Tip 104: Where are most pigs raised in the states?

The highest percentage of the country's pigs are produced in Iowa.

Tip 105: What is the most common pig breed in the US?

Yorkshire is the most commonly bred and raised hog in the US.

Tip 106: Where do hogs come from?

Modern pigs' ancestors come from being imported to the United States from the county of Hampshire, England. However, it is believed that the breed originated from Northern England and Scotland.

About the Author

Keiren Cook is a young and avid writer who is passionate about raising quality hogs for the youth interested in agriculture. She started in the hog business as a freshman in high school when she showed her first hog at the county fair. From there, her love for hogs has grown into a thriving business, where for the last six years, she has built up a reputation for breeding and producing high-quality meat and show hogs for the youth in her community. Over those six years, she has been in many experiences and situations, which has prepared her to write an information-dense "How-To" book about raising this breed of livestock.

HowExpert publishes how to guides by everyday experts. Visit HowExpert.com to learn more.

Recommended Resources

- HowExpert.com – Quick 'How To' Guides on All Topics from A to Z by Everyday Experts.
- HowExpert.com/free – Free HowExpert Email Newsletter.
- HowExpert.com/books – HowExpert Books
- HowExpert.com/courses – HowExpert Courses
- HowExpert.com/clothing – HowExpert Clothing
- HowExpert.com/membership – HowExpert Membership Site
- HowExpert.com/affiliates – HowExpert Affiliate Program
- HowExpert.com/jobs – HowExpert Jobs
- HowExpert.com/writers – Write About Your #1 Passion/Knowledge/Expertise & Become a HowExpert Author.
- HowExpert.com/resources – Additional HowExpert Recommended Resources
- YouTube.com/HowExpert – Subscribe to HowExpert YouTube.
- Instagram.com/HowExpert – Follow HowExpert on Instagram.
- Facebook.com/HowExpert – Follow HowExpert on Facebook.
- TikTok.com/@HowExpert – Follow HowExpert on TikTok.

Made in the USA
Monee, IL
21 June 2024

60301292R00100